THE SPURS QUIZ BOOK

Covering the 80s, 90s and 2000s

UNOFFICIAL AND UNAUTHORISED

THE SPURS QUIZ BOOK

Covering the 80s, 90s and 2000s

Compiled by Chris Cowlin

Foreword by Chas Hodges

APEX PUBLISHING LTD

First published in hardback in 2010 by

Apex Publishing Ltd
PO Box 7086, Clacton on Sea, Essex, CO15 5WN, England
www.apexpublishing.co.uk

British Library Cataloguing-in-Publication Data
A catalogue record for this book
is available from the British Library

ISBN: 1-906358-86-9   978-1-906358-86-0

Typeset in 10.5pt Chianti Bdlt Win95BT

Cover Design: Siobhan Smith

Printed and bound in Great Britain by
the MPG Books Group in the UK

Special Note: This book is in no way connected to Tottenham Hotspur Football Club. It is unofficial and unauthorised.

Dedication:
This book is dedicated to my dad, Martin. We have been to many Spurs matches together - some great memories.

FOREWORD

I never became a Spurs fan; I was born a Spurs fan - just around the corner from the ground, in the North Middlesex Hospital, Edmonton, in 1943. If I'd been born a bit further down the road, I would've been born an Arsenal fan! That's the way it was in those days. You supported your local team. I still do a double take when someone younger than me states in a cockney accent that he supports "Man U". It doesn't make sense.

I first went 'up the Spurs' with my older brother, Dave, around 1954, but not to see the first team. Back in those days there was a reserve match every other week, which would pull around five to six thousand people, compared with the forty to fifty thousand at first team matches. Mum was worried about our safety among the huge crowds, so she would only let us go to reserve matches. Then we turned up one Saturday to find that the first team were playing. When we got home we told mum what a great time we'd had and how we were now "old enough to look after ourselves among big crowds". So from then on we were allowed to go up the Spurs with the big boys.

I played in goal for Eldon Road School and the Spurs goalie then, Ted Ditchburn, was my hero. He'd played a couple of games for England, but I thought he should've been England's permanent goalkeeper. Alf Ramsey was Spurs' left back at that time. Whenever he got the ball he always did something useful with it. A master penalty taker, I never saw him miss. I remember Danny Blanchflower's first game. He didn't kick a ball, he placed it, like a chess player. Some of Glenn Hoddle's style later on reminded me of Danny.

When music took over and I began to learn guitar in 1956, Spurs took a back seat. Although I've always had a warm feeling for Spurs and am pleased when they're doing well, music has always come first. I never ever saw the Double side in the sixties live, as I was on the road touring and enjoying the life. I still am. I remember my mum one day saying, "You coming down the road to see the Spurs parade the Double?" But I was too busy learning a new Jerry Lee bit on the piano. Nevertheless, Spurs are in my blood and always will be.

Leaping on to the eighties, Dave and me were signed to a management company run by Bob England, a massive Spurs fan. Every time you spoke to him on the phone, the first five - or sometimes thirty - minutes were given over to opinions and critical rundowns of Tottenham's last match. Then business would start. I remember touring Australia in the eighties in the days of not-so-good electrical means of communication and Bob ringing up a pal and asking him to put the phone next to his radio for the whole second half of a Spurs commentary. I don't know what the bill was. Come to think of it, he phoned from my hotel room. I've ... no, too late now.

It was Bob who suggested we should write a song for Spurs. 'Ossie's Dream' was his suggestion for a title. "That's the buzz going on down the Spurs," said Bob. "Ossie's dream is to play at Wembley."

Dave and me agreed to the idea in principle, but I had other things on my mind. I was doing string arrangements, brass arrangements ... we were in the middle of an album, for Christ's sake!

So Dave took over. He came up with: "Ossie's going to Wembley/His knees have gone all Trembley." I thought the 'Trembley' bit was sort of 'dunno about that', and Dave wasn't 100% sure either - "but I can't think of anything else that rhymes with Wembley," he said. Then Bob informed us that the team played the demo on the coach and fell about. So 'Trembley' was in.

In the recording studio I spoke to Ossie.

"This is your solo bit: 'In de cup for Tottingham'," I said.

Ossie replied, "But I can say 'Tottenham' now."

"But we want you to say 'Tottingham!' The way you used to say it!"

And so he did - magnificently.

But by far the funniest line we ever got anybody to sing was Nico Clausen's line on the B side of 'Hot Shot Tottenham' (1987 Cup final). It was supposed to be funny, but Nico's unawareness made it unforgettably so. And so was Ossie's reaction, actually collapsing with laughter on the studio floor. Nico Clausen looked a little bit annoyed. He didn't really know what was going on.

Nico's line to Ossie was: "Are you gonna play a blinder?" But his delivery was so hilarious that the whole Spurs team collapsed with laughter. Ossie's response was supposed to be: "I do my best for Tottingham, mate." But Ossie couldn't get it out! We had to overdub it later.

Nico couldn't see the funny side of it, which made it even funnier. He was Belgian. 'Play a blinder?' What the (!) did that mean? But it wasn't the line, it was the way he'd done it!

Spurs lost to Coventry that year, so the record never sold a lot, which means that today that Spurs record is the most collectable because not many were pressed up. So if you've got a copy, look after it! But play the B side every now and then and fall about at dear ol' Nico's line.

So there you are. It was all fun and good football. Even the bad times were good. And, by the way, let me tell you, those boys loved it on Top of the Pops! What a team!

And now, at last, here is a quiz book that is devoted to the finest football club in the world: Tottenham Hotspur!

Best wishes
Chas Hodges

INTRODUCTION

I would first of all like to thank Chas Hodges for writing the foreword to this book; Chas and Dave have performed some great songs for Tottenham over the years so I was delighted when he agreed to write a piece for the book.

I would also like to thank all the former players, newspapers, magazines, etc, for their kind comments about this book.

Tottenham Hotspur Football Club has been a big part of my life, supporting them since I was 10 years old when I was first introduced to Spurs from my school friend Tom Luesley. It was a good choice as most of my family supported Arsenal, and still do!

My first match to 'The Lane' was in May 1994, a 2-1 defeat against QPR, the final day of the 1993/1994 season.

The 1994/1995 season remains my favourite season as a Spurs fan, seeing Jürgen Klinsmann play was tremendous and very memorable. I will never forget the game against Aston Villa in November 1994, a 4-3 defeat, Gerry Francis' first game in charge at the club – what a game that was; my Dad and I have never been off our seats so much!

I have met a lot of Spurs players over the years and Jürgen Klinsmann still remains my favourite, he always had time for the fans and is a true gentleman.

This book is focused on the last 30 years of football – covering the 1980s, 1990s and 2000s; I would like to think it has something in it for everyone.

This book has been a real joy to compile and I hope you

enjoy testing your knowledge of this great club. Hopefully it should bring back some wonderful memories!

In closing, I would like to thank all my friends and family for encouraging me to complete this book.

Best wishes
Chris Cowlin

JÜRGEN KLINSMANN

1. Which Spurs manager signed Jürgen when he joined the club in 1994?

2. How many League goals did Jürgen score for Tottenham during the 1994/95 season, having played in 41 matches?

3. Against which team did Jürgen score his first goal for Spurs, in a 4-3 away win on his debut in the Premier League?

4. Against which team did Jürgen score a brace for Tottenham, in a 2-1 win on his home debut?

5. Jürgen signed on loan from which club when he joined Spurs for his second playing spell in December 1997?

6. Who was Jürgen's strike partner at Spurs during the 1994/95 season?

7. In which year was Jürgen born – 1962, 1963 or 1964?

8. How many League goals has Jürgen scored for Spurs in his career – 29, 39 or 49?

9. Which German team did Jürgen join when he left White Hart Lane in May 2005 after his first spell at the club?

10. In what year did Jürgen become manager of Germany?

HARRY REDKNAPP

11. True or false: Harry once played a League game for Spurs during his playing days?

12. In what year did Harry take charge at White Hart Lane?

13. Harry took over from which manager at White Hart Lane?

14. Harry led Spurs to the final of which Cup in his first season at the club?

15. Which team did Spurs beat 2-0 at home when Harry managed the club for the first time in the Premier League?

16. Which Tottenham chairman appointed Harry as club manager?

17. Which striker did Harry sign for Spurs from his previous club, Portsmouth, during July 2009?

18. Can you name the London club that Harry has both played for and managed in his career?

19. In which year was Harry born in London – 1945, 1946 or 1947?

20. To what position in the Premier League did Harry guide Tottenham during his first season in charge at the club?

2009/2010

21. Which team did Spurs beat 2-1 on the opening day of the League season at White Hart Lane?

22. Which striker scored a Spurs hat-trick in a 5-1 away League win against Hull City during August 2009?

23. Which team did Tottenham beat 5-0 at home, with Robbie Keane grabbing four of the goals, during September 2009?

24. How many of Tottenham's nine goals did Jermain Defoe score in their 9-1 home League win against Wigan Athletic during November 2009?

25. With which London team did Spurs share a 0-0 away draw on Boxing Day 2009?

26. Can you name Tottenham's two goalscorers in the 2-0 home League win over West Ham during December 2009?

27. Which striker came off the bench to score a brace away at Wigan Athletic in Tottenham's 3-0 League win?

28. Which French defender did Spurs sign from Newcastle United during August 2009?

29. For which club did Darren Bent sign when he left White Hart Lane in August 2009?

30. Who wore the number 15 shirt for Tottenham during this season?

HONOURS

Match up the honour with the year it was achieved

31.	FA Cup Winners	2008
32.	Charity Shield Winners (joint)	2005
33.	League Cup Winners	1984
34.	Charity Shield Winners (joint)	1990
35.	FA Cup Winners	1992
36.	Peace Cup (Korea) Winners	1991
37.	League Cup Winners	1982
38.	FA Youth Cup Winners	1981
39.	FA Cup Winners	1999
40.	UEFA Cup Winners	1982

LEGENDS – 1

Rearrange the letters to reveal the name of a club legend

41.   LENNG OLDHED

42.   DEDYT HIGHERMANS

43.   SISOE DERAILS

44.   KYRCI LAVLI

45.   VADDI INGOAL

46.   YGRA BABTTUM

47.   NEARJIM FEEDO

48.   ARY CELMENEC

49.   RHGTA ORSOCK

50.   AIN ELKWAR

FA CUP WINNERS – 1991

51. Which team did Spurs beat in the FA Cup final?

52. Who played in goal for Tottenham in the FA Cup final?

53. What was the score in the FA Cup final?

54. Which England left back put the opponents 1-0 up, scoring a trademark free kick?

55. Can you name the two substitutes that Spurs used in the FA Cup final?

56. Which goalkeeper saved Gary Lineker's penalty in the FA Cup final?

57. Can you name seven of Tottenham's starting eleven in the FA Cup final?

58. Which opponents' defender scored an own goal in extra time, giving Tottenham their second and winning goal in the FA Cup final?

59. Which Tottenham manager guided the club to this success?

60. Which London rivals did Spurs beat in the FA Cup semi-final at Wembley?

MANAGERS

Match up the manager with the year he took charge at White Hart Lane

61.	Terry Venables	1993
62.	Gerry Francis	1992
63.	George Graham	2004
64.	Glenn Hoddle	1987
65.	Martin Jol	1986
66.	Christian Gross	1994
67.	Doug Livermore	1997
68.	Juande Ramos	1998
69.	David Pleat	2001
70.	Ossie Ardiles	2007

FIRST PREMIER LEAGUE SEASON – 1992/1993

71.   With which club did Spurs share a 0-0 away draw in
        their first ever Premier League match during August
        1992?

72.   True or false: Spurs had to wait until their sixth
        Premier League match before they recorded their first
        win?

73.   Which striker scored a brace against Arsenal at
        Highbury in a 3-1 win during May 1993?

74.   How many of their 42 Premier League matches did the
        club win – 12, 14 or 16?

75.   Which striker did Spurs sign from Nottingham Forest
        during August 1992?

76.   Against which team did Teddy Sheringham score a
        Spurs hat-trick in a 4-0 home League win during
        February 1993?

77.   Which team did Spurs beat 4-2 at home during
        February 1993, scoring all their goals in five minutes,
        having been 1-0 down after an Iain Dowie goal?

78.   Who scored Tottenham's goal in a 1-1 draw against
        Manchester United at White Hart Lane in the Premier
        League during September 1992?

79.   In what position in the Premier League did Spurs
        finish?

80.   Which striker scored a brace for Spurs in a 5-1 home
        win against Norwich City in the Premier League during
        April 1993?

LEAGUE GOALS – 1

Match up the player with the number of League goals he scored in his Tottenham career

81.	Chris Armstrong	18
82.	Darren Anderton	60
83.	Paul Allen	10
84.	Nico Claesen	20
85.	Sol Campbell	34
86.	Guy Butters	27
87.	Darren Bent	48
88.	Dimitar Berbatov	18
89.	Nick Barmby	1
90.	Clive Allen	23

WHERE DID THEY COME FROM? – 1

*Match up the player with his previous club
before joining Tottenham*

91.	Niko Kranjčar	Southampton
92.	Carlo Cudicini	Charlton Athletic
93.	David Bentley	PSV Eindhoven
94.	Aaron Lennon	Cardiff City
95.	Danny Murphy	Portsmouth
96.	Edgar Davids	Leeds United
97.	Gareth Bale	Chelsea
98.	Darren Bent	Blackburn Rovers
99.	Chris Gunter	Inter Milan
100.	Heurelho Gomes	Charlton Athletic

JERMAIN DEFOE

101. What is Jermain's middle name – Colin, Chesney or Conroy?

102. From which London club did Jermain sign when he joined Spurs in 2004?

103. What squad number did Jermain wear for Tottenham during the 2009/10 season?

104. Which team did Spurs beat 4-3 at home, with Jermain scoring the club's first goal on his League debut during February 2004?

105. For which team did Jermain sign when he left White Hart Lane in January 2008 before returning to The Lane in January 2009?

106. For which London team did Jermain play between 1999 and 2004?

107. Against which team did Jermain score a winning 45th-minute goal for Tottenham before getting sent off after 60 minutes in a 2-1 away League win during October 2009?

108. Against which team did Jermain score a hat-trick in Tottenham's 3-1 away win in the FA Cup 4th round replay during February 2010?

109. How many League goals did Jermain score for Spurs during the 2004/05 season – 9, 11 or 13?

110. Against which country did Jermain score a brace in England's 2-2 friendly away match during August 2009?

TEDDY SHERINGHAM

111. Against which team did Teddy score his first Spurs League goal, in a 2-0 home win in the Premier League during August 1992?

112. How many League hat-tricks did Teddy score for Spurs in his first season at White Hart Lane?

113. For which club did Teddy play in between his two playing spells at Tottenham?

114. Can you name the other two London clubs that Teddy played for in his football career?

115. How many League goals did Teddy score for Spurs in his 42 appearances during the 1994/95 season – 16, 18 or 20?

116. In which year was Teddy born in London – 1965, 1966 or 1967?

117. Against which team did Teddy score a League hat-trick in Tottenham's 4-0 home win during December 1994, with Gica Popescu scoring Spurs' other goal in the game?

118. How many League appearances did Teddy make for Spurs in his playing days – 236, 239 or 242?

119. Which Spurs manager signed Teddy in 2001 for his second playing spell at The Lane, this being one of the manager's first signings?

120. How many League goals did Teddy score in his Tottenham career – 95, 97 or 99?

2008/2009

121. Which Spurs midfielder scored a brace in a 4-0 home win against Middlesbrough during March 2009?

122. What was the score when Spurs visited The Emirates Stadium to play Arsenal during October 2008?

123. Which striker scored a brace when Spurs beat Wigan 3-1 during January 2009 at White Hart Lane?

124. Who started the League season as Tottenham manager but was replaced in October 2008?

125. Which French defender joined Tottenham for his second spell at the club during January 2009, signing from Sunderland?

126. Which striker finished the season as the club's highest scorer with 12 League goals?

127. Which team did Spurs beat 2-1, with Roman Pavlyuchenko scoring a 90th-minute winner, during November 2008?

128. Which goalkeeper did Spurs sign on a free transfer from Chelsea during January 2009?

129. Which Spurs player scored the only goal in a 1-0 home win over West Ham United at White Hart Lane during April 2009?

130. In what position in the Premier League did Spurs finish – 7th 8th or 9th

OSSIE ARDILES

131. How many League goals did Ossie score for Tottenham in his career – 6, 16 or 26?

132. Ossie appeared in which 1981 film alongside football legends Pelé and Bobby Moore?

133. Against which team did Ossie make his Spurs debut, in a 1-1 League away draw during August 1978?

134. Can you name the three English sides that Ossie played for after leaving Tottenham, in the late 1980s?

135. True or false: Ossie wore the number 1 shirt for his country in the 1982 World Cup?

136. How many League goals did Ossie score for Spurs during the 1980/81 season?

137. Can you name the three winners' medals that Ossie won whilst a Tottenham player?

138. How many League games did Ossie play for Tottenham in his playing career – 238, 258 or 278?

139. In what year was Ossie appointed as Tottenham manager?

140. What nationality is Ossie?

LES FERDINAND

141. How many England caps did Les win for England, scoring five goals?

142. Against which London team did Les score the 10,000th goal in Premier League history during December 2001 in a 4-0 home win for Spurs?

143. Against which team did Les score a Spurs hat-trick in a 6-0 home win in the League Cup quarter-final during December 2001?

144. Which Spurs manager signed Les for Tottenham in 1997?

145. Against which London team did Les score his first Tottenham League goal, in only his second game for the club, in a 2-1 away defeat during August 1997?

146. In what position did Les play during his playing days?

147. How many League goals did Les score for Spurs in his career – 22, 33 or 44?

148. Against which Midlands club did Les score a brace for Spurs in a 3-2 home League win during August 1997?

149. What was the only medal that Les won whilst a player at White Hart Lane?

150. From which team did Les join Tottenham in 1997?

2007/2008

151. In what position did Spurs finish in the League this season?

152. Can you name the two strikers that finished the season with 15 League goals?

153. With which London team did Tottenham draw 4-4 at White Hart Lane in the League during March 2008?

154. Which striker scored a brace for Spurs in a 4-0 home win in the Premier League during March 2008?

155. Which Brazilian defender did Spurs sign from German side Hertha Berlin during January 2008?

156. What was the score when Manchester United visited White Hart Lane in the Premier League during February 2008?

157. Which Spurs striker scored four goals against Reading in Tottenham's 6-4 League win at The Lane during December 2007?

158. Which two players both scored a brace for Spurs in their 5-1 home win against Fulham on Boxing Day 2007?

159. Which defender did Spurs sign from Middlesbrough during January 2008?

160. Which French defender scored Tottenham's last-minute equaliser in a 4-4 home League draw during October 2007?

LEAGUE APPEARANCES – 1

Match up the player with the number of League appearances he made for Spurs in his career

161.	David Tuttle	37 (22)
162.	Terry Yorath	20 (6)
163.	Sergei Rebrov	48 (13)
164.	David Kerslake	257 (2)
165.	Kazuyuki Toda	45 (2)
166.	Luke Young	10 (3)
167.	Andy Reid	44 (4)
168.	Ian Walker	34 (3)
169.	Neil Ruddock	44 (14)
170.	Teemu Tainio	2 (2)

POT LUCK – 1

171. What are Tottenham's two nicknames?

172. In what year did Daniel Levy replace Alan Sugar as club chairman?

173. What does the club's Latin motto 'Audere est Facere' mean?

174. Which company were the shirt sponsors between 1995 and 1999, taking over from Holsten?

175. How many times did the club win the FA Cup during the 1980s?

176. Spurs won the League Cup four times, but in which years?

177. Can you name the first ever French manager to take charge of Spurs in their history?

178. Who was voted the club's Player of the Year for the 2009/10 season?

179. In which part of London are Spurs situated – central, north or south?

180. In which season did Spurs win the FA Premier Reserve League South Championship – 2003/04, 2005/06 or 2007/08?

CHRIS ARMSTRONG

181. How many League goals did Chris score for Tottenham in his career – 48, 58 or 68?

182. From which club did Spurs sign Chris during June 1995 for £4.5 million?

183. True or false: it took Chris until his 9th League match for Spurs to score his first Tottenham League goal?

184. Against which team did Chris score a brace in a 4-1 home League win on New Year's Day 1996?

185. In which year was Chris born in Newcastle – 1970, 1971 or 1972?

186. Against which team did Chris score a Tottenham brace in a 2-0 away League win during August 1996?

187. How many of Tottenham's goals did Chris score in the 7-2 home League win against Southampton during March 2000?

188. For which Welsh team did Chris play between 1989 and 1991?

189. Against which team did Chris score Spurs' only goal in the 23rd minute at The Lane in a 1-0 home League win during January 2000?

190. Which Spurs manager signed Chris for Tottenham?

LEAGUE APPEARANCES – 2

*Match up the player with the number of League
appearances he made for Spurs in his career*

191.	Dean Richards	29 (4)
192.	Jamie Redknapp	16 (2)
193.	Garry Brady	46 (8)
194.	Gary Lineker	3 (10)
195.	Erik Edman	12 (8)
196.	Moussa Saïb	0 (9)
197.	Kevin Scott	31
198.	John Scales	37 (11)
199.	Johnnie Jackson	105
200.	Øyvind Leonhardsen	73

LEGENDS – 2

Re-arrange the letters to reveal the name of a club legend

201.   LUPA NEALL

202.   IBEBRO ENKEA

203.   YELLED GINK

204.   EOJ ARKNINE

205.   ESVET MYNAPERR

206.   YGRA REINELK

207.   LAUP INCAGESGO

208.   VILEC NELAL

209.   SHIRC HOGHUNT

210.   DIDVA SOWHELL

POT LUCK - 2

211. True or false: Spurs won the FA Youth Cup during the 1989/90 season?

212. Who was the first ever foreign manager of Tottenham?

213. What nationality was manager Christian Gross?

214. Who were the club's shirt sponsors between 2002 and 2006?

215. True or false: the first ever Tottenham kit comprised a navy blue shirt and shorts?

216. Which Spurs player won the Player of the Year award for the 2008/09 season?

217. Which year marked the club's 125th anniversary – 2006, 2007 or 2008?

218. What club record transfer fee did Tottenham pay Dynamo Kiev for Sergei Rebrov in 2000?

219. In what year was the club renamed 'Tottenham Hotspur Football and Athletic Club'?

220. Who was the club's kit manufacturer between 1978 and 1980?

CLIVE ALLEN

221. True or false: Clive was a striker during his playing days at White Hart Lane?

222. Clive signed from which club when he joined Spurs in 1984?

223. In which year was Clive born in Stepney – 1961, 1963 or 1965?

224. Who was Clive's father, a former Tottenham striker in the early 1960s?

225. How many League appearances did Clive make for Spurs in his career - 85, 95 or 105?

226. What is Clive's middle name – Darren, Daniel or David?

227. Against which team did Clive make his Spurs League debut, in a 4-1 win away during August 1984, scoring twice in the game?

228. Which manager signed Clive for Tottenham?

229. How many League goals did Clive score for Spurs in his career – 40, 60 or 80?

230. For which French club did Clive sign when he left The Lane in 1988?

WHERE DID THEY COME FROM? – 2

Match up the player with his previous club before joining Tottenham

231.	Steve Hodge	Coventry City
232.	Richard Gough	Southend United
233.	Bobby Mimms	Queens Park Rangers
234.	Paul Walsh	PSV Eindhoven
235.	Steve Sedgley	Nottingham Forest
236.	Justin Edinburgh	Aston Villa
237.	Pat Van Den Hauwe	Dundee United
238.	Teddy Sheringham	Liverpool
239.	Clive Wilson	Everton
240.	Gica Popescu	Everton

GARETH BALE

241.   For which country is Gareth a full international?

242.   Which squad number did Gareth wear for Spurs during the 2009/10 season?

243.   From which club did Gareth sign when he joined Tottenham in 2007?

244.   Against which three teams did Gareth score his three Premier League goals of the 2009/10 season?

245.   Against which team did Gareth score his first Tottenham goal, in a 3-3 away League draw during September 2007?

246.   In which year was Gareth born in Cardiff – 1988, 1989 or 1990?

247.   How many League goals did Gareth score for Spurs in his first season at the club?

248.   Can you name one of the two awards that Gareth won during 2007?

249.   What is Gareth's middle name – Frank, Freddie or Francis?

250.   True or false: Gareth won the 'Young Player of the Year' during the 2009/10 season at The Lane?

LEAGUE GOALS – 2

Match up the player with the number of League goals he scored in his Tottenham career

251.	Simon Davies	20
252.	Stephen Kelly	13
253.	Micky Hazard	4
254.	Tony Galvin	68
255.	Gary Doherty	13
256.	Terry Fenwick	13
257.	Mark Falco	2
258.	Ilie Dumitrescu	8
259.	Ruel Fox	4
260.	Jason Dozzell	15

2006/2007

261. In what position did Spurs finish in the Premier League?

262. Which defender did Tottenham sign from Benfica during January 2007?

263. Which striker finished as the club's highest League scorer with 12 goals?

264. Can you name the two Spurs players that scored in a 2-1 home League win over Chelsea during November 2006?

265. Which London team did Tottenham beat 5-1 at The Lane during December 2006?

266. Which striker scored a brace for Spurs in a 3-2 away win against Middlesbrough during April 2007?

267. Which Spurs midfielder scored Tottenham's last-minute equaliser in a 2-2 home draw against Arsenal during April 2007?

268. Which Canadian defender scored Tottenham's winner in a 4-3 away win against West Ham during March 2007?

269. Which team did Spurs beat 2-1 at The Lane on Boxing Day 2006, with Jermain Defoe scoring a brace in the game?

270. Who played in goal for Spurs during their 38 League games of this season?

DIMITAR BERBATOV

271. For which country was Dimitar a full international when he signed for Tottenham?

272. From which German team did Dimitar join Spurs in 2006?

273. Against which team did Dimitar score his first Spurs goal, in his home League debut in a 2-0 win during August 2006?

274. Against which London team did Dimitar score a Spurs brace in a 4-0 away FA Cup 5th round win during February 2007?

275. How many of Tottenham's six goals did Dimitar score in their 6-4 home League win against Reading during December 2007?

276. In which year was Dimitar born – 1979, 1981 or 1983?

277. True or false: Dimitar scored Spurs' two goals in their FA Cup 3rd round 2-2 home draw against Reading during January 2008?

278. How many League goals did Dimitar score for Tottenham in his career – 23, 25 or 27?

279. In what year did Dimitar leave White Hart Lane to join Manchester United?

280. How much did Spurs pay for Dimitar in 2006 – £9.9 million, £10.9 million or £11.9 million?

DAVID GINOLA

281. How many League goals did David score for Spurs in his career –13, 14 or 15?

282. Which Midlands team did David join when he left White Hart Lane in 2000?

283. Which two awards did David win in 1999 whilst a Tottenham player?

284. What was the only winners' medal that David won whilst a Spurs player?

285. In which year was David born in France – 1966, 1967 or 1968?

286. True or false: David only ever started League matches for Tottenham and was never used as a substitute during his career at White Hart Lane?

287. From which club did David join Tottenham in July 1997?

288. Against which team did David score his first Tottenham goal, in a 2-0 League Cup, 2nd round, 2nd leg away win during September 1997?

289. How many League games did David play for Spurs – 99, 100 or 101?

290. Against which Yorkshire team did David score a Spurs brace in a 3-0 home League win during December 1997, scoring in the 12th and 18th minutes?

2005/2006

291.   True or false: Spurs were unbeaten in their first three League matches and didn't concede a League goal?

292.   Which Lancashire team did Spurs beat 2-0 on Boxing Day 2005, with Robbie Keane scoring a penalty and Jermain Defoe scoring in the last minute of the game?

293.   Who scored Tottenham's goal against Arsenal in a 1-1 League away draw during April 2006?

294.   Which goalkeeper played in all 38 League matches for Spurs this season?

295.   With how many League goals did Robbie Keane end the season, finishing as the club's highest scorer - 16, 17 or 18?

296.   In what position did Spurs finish in the Premier League?

297.   Which Tottenham player scored the only goal at The Lane in their 1-0 home win against Bolton Wanderers during April 2006?

298.   Which Spurs midfielder scored the club's winner at home in a 3-2 League win against Sunderland during December 2005?

299.   Who was Tottenham's manager during this season?

300.   Which Tottenham striker scored the club's winner in a 3-2 away win against Charlton Athletic during October 2005 after being 2-0 down?

SPURS IN THE FA CUP

301. Spurs have won this competition eight times, but can you name the years?

302. Which team beat Spurs 1-0 in the semi-finals at Wembley during the 1992/93 season?

303. Spurs drew 1-1 at home to Newcastle United in the 3rd round during December 1999, but what was the score in the 3rd round replay at St James' Park, played 10 days later?

304. In which round of the competition did Everton knock Spurs out of the FA Cup during the 1985/86 season?

305. Which team beat Tottenham 4-1 in the FA Cup semi-final at Elland Road during April 1995?

306. Which Tottenham player scored a hat-trick against Manchester City in a 4-2 away win during March 1993 in the FA Cup quarter-finals?

307. Which London team did Spurs beat 3-2 away in the quarter-finals during March 2001, with Sergei Rebrov scoring a brace and Gary Doherty scoring the other Spurs goal?

308. Can you name the Spurs striker who scored the only goal in a 1-0 away win against Reading in the 3rd round replay during January 2008?

309. Which team knocked Spurs out of the competition in the 4th round during January 2009, beating Spurs 2-1 at home?

310. In which year did Spurs finish as runners-up in this competition?

LEAGUE GOALS – 3

Match up the player with the number of League goals he scored in his Tottenham career

311.	Dean Marney	1
312.	Steed Malbranque	1
313.	Mbulelo Mabizela	31
314.	Steve Perryman	1
315.	Noé Pamarot	13
316.	Noureddine Naybet	2
317.	Nayim	1
318.	John Moncur	6
319.	Mido	11
320.	Pedro Mendes	1

WHERE DID THEY GO? – 1

Match up the player with the club he joined
after leaving White Hart Lane

321.	Kevin Boateng	Liverpool
322.	Gordon Durie	Luton Town
323.	John Polston	Portsmouth
324.	Paul Walsh	Rangers
325.	Paul Stewart	Nottingham Forest
326.	John Moncur	Norwich City
327.	Phil Gray	Norwich City
328.	Richard Gough	Swindon Town
329.	Chris Gunter	Portsmouth
330.	Ian Crook	Rangers

LEAGUE GOALS – 4

*Match up the player with the number of League
goals he scored in his Tottenham career*

331.	Andy Reid	4
332.	Graham Roberts	3
333.	Ronny Rosenthal	7
334.	Neil Ruddock	18
335.	Paul Stewart	23
336.	Paul Stalteri	28
337.	Andy Turner	2
338.	Ramon Vega	2
339.	Ricardo Villa	1
340.	Mauricio Taricco	3

SPURS IN THE LEAGUE CUP

341. Spurs have won the competition four times, but can you recall the years?

342. What was the score when Spurs played Arsenal in the semi-final, 2nd leg, at White Hart Lane during January 2008?

343. Which striker scored a Tottenham brace in the club's 4-0 home win against Chester City in the 2nd round, 1st leg, during September 1995?

344. Which defender scored a 90th-minute winner in the club's 2-1 3rd round home win against Sunderland during October 1996?

345. Which Essex side did Tottenham beat 1-0 at White Hart Lane in the quarter-finals, after extra time, with Jermain Defoe scoring after 115 minutes, during December 2006?

346. Which team did Spurs beat 5-0 at home in the 2nd round, 1st leg, during September 1990?

347. Which Spurs midfielder scored the only goal in the club's 1-0 3rd round away win against Manchester City during October 1992?

348. Which team did Spurs beat 6-0 away from home in the 2nd round during September 2004, with Frederic Kanoute (2), Robbie Keane, Jermain Defoe, Goran Bunjevčević and Anthony Gardner scoring the goals?

349. What was the score when Spurs played Doncaster Rovers away in the 2nd round during August 2009?

350. In what year during the 1980s were Spurs runner-ups in the competition?

WHERE DID THEY COME FROM? – 3

*Match up the player with his previous club
before joining Tottenham*

351.	John Scales	Sporting Lisbon
352.	Ramon Vega	Wimbledon
353.	José Dominguez	Ipswich Town
354.	Nicola Berti	Luton Town
355.	Mauricio Taricco	Liverpool
356.	Anthony Gardner	Wimbledon
357.	Gary Doherty	Liverpool
358.	Neil Sullivan	Inter Milan
359.	Chris Perry	Cagliari
360.	Øyvind Leonhardsen	Port Vale

LEAGUE CUP FINALISTS - 2009

361. Which team beat Spurs in the final, winning 4-1 on penalties after extra time?

362. What was the score after 120 minutes played?

363. What was the attendance in the League Cup final, played at Wembley – 78,217, 83,217 or 88,217?

364. Which Tottenham opponent won the Man of the Match award in the game?

365. Who were Tottenham's two centre backs during the final?

366. Can you name two of the three Spurs substitutes used in the game?

367. Who was Tottenham's manager on the day of the League Cup final?

368. How many of Tottenham's starting eleven in the final were English?

369. In what month of the year was the final played?

370. Which team did Spurs beat 6-4 on aggregate in the semi-finals?

WHERE DID THEY GO? – 2

*Match up the player with the club he joined
after leaving White Hart Lane*

371.	Gudni Bergsson	Queens Park Rangers
372.	Gica Popescu	Ipswich Town
373.	Kevin Scott	Reading
374.	Dean Austin	Everton
375.	Ronny Rosenthal	Norwich City
376.	Clive Wilson	Bolton Wanderers
377.	Jason Cundy	Watford
378.	Steve Slade	Barcelona
379.	Darren Caskey	Crystal Palace
380.	Vinny Samways	Cambridge United

LEAGUE CUP WINNERS - 2008

381. Which London team did Tottenham beat in the League Cup final at Wembley?

382. Which manager led Spurs to this success?

383. Who played in goal for Spurs in the final?

384. What was the score after 90 minutes in the final?

385. Which Spurs striker scored Tottenham's equaliser in the 70th minute from the penalty spot?

386. Can you name the two French players that started the final for Spurs?

387. True or false: the attendance in the final was 87,660?

388. Who refereed the League Cup final, played in February 2008?

389. True or false: this was the first League Cup final to be played at the new Wembley Stadium, and the first to be played in England since the old Wembley was demolished in 2000?

390. Which Spurs defender scored the club's winner in extra time, heading in from a Jermaine Jenas free kick?

WHERE DID THEY GO? – 3

*Match up the player with the club he joined
after leaving White Hart Lane*

391.	Ramon Vega	Norwich City
392.	Milenko Ačimovič	Leicester City
393.	Chris Perry	Hull City
394.	Gary Doherty	Chelsea
395.	Steffen Iversen	Southampton
396.	Stephen Clemence	Lille
397.	Ben Thatcher	Wolves
398.	Jamie Redknapp	Charlton Athletic
399.	Neil Sullivan	Watford
400.	Alton Thelwell	Birmingham City

TERRY VENABLES

401. How many League goals did Terry score for Tottenham in his playing career – 3, 5 or 7?

402. True or false: Terry was Spurs manager when Tottenham won the FA Cup in 1991?

403. To what position in the League did Terry guide Spurs in his first season in charge at White Hart Lane during 1987/88?

404. Which Spurs manager signed Terry for the club in 1966?

405. How many League appearances did Terry make for Spurs in his playing career - 115, 135 or 155?

406. From which London team did Terry sign for Tottenham in 1966?

407. What is Terry's nickname?

408. Which team did Terry manage between 1994 and1996?

409. What was the only winners' medal that Terry picked up during his playing days at White Hart Lane?

410. In which year was Terry born in Dagenham – 1941, 1942 or 1943?

2004/2005

411. Can you name the three Spurs players, all with sur names beginning with 'K', who scored in the club's 5-1 home League win against Aston Villa during May 2005?

412. What was the score when Spurs visited Norwich City at Carrow Road on Boxing Day 2004?

413. Which midfielder scored a Tottenham brace, his only Spurs career goals, in their 5-2 home League win against Everton during January 2005?

414. Which team did Tottenham play on the opening day of the League season, drawing 1-1 at White Hart Lane on 14 August 2004?

415. Which defender did Tottenham sign during January 2005 from Nottingham Forest?

416. Can you name the two strikers who scored double figures in League competition for Tottenham during this season?

417. Which goalkeeper started the two League games that Paul Robinson missed during this season, away at Middlesbrough and at home against Blackburn Rovers, both during May 2005?

418. How many of their 38 League matches did Tottenham win - 14, 16 or 18?

419. Which midfielder did Spurs sign from West Ham United during August 2004?

420. Which striker scored a hat-trick in the club's 5-1 home League win against Southampton during December 2004?

GARTH CROOKS

421. True or false: Garth was awarded an OBE in 1999 for his services to football punditry?

422. Can you name the three winners' medals that Garth won whilst a Tottenham player?

423. What is Garth's middle name – Anthony, Alistair or Arnold?

424. In what year did Garth sign for Spurs from Stoke City?

425. How many League goals did Garth score for Spurs in his first season at White Hart Lane, his best tally for Tottenham in his career?

426. Against which team did Garth make his Spurs League debut, scoring in a 2-0 home win?

427. In what position did Garth play during his playing days?

428. How many League goals did Garth score for Tottenham in his career - 46, 48 or 50?

429. True or false: Garth became the first black chairman of the Professional Footballers' Association in 1988?

430. For which team did Garth sign when he left White Hart Lane in 1985?

LEAGUE CUP WINNERS - 1999

431. Which team did Tottenham beat 1-0 at Wembley in the League Cup final?

432. Who scored Tottenham's only goal in the last minute of the final?

433. Which Spurs manager led the club to this success?

434. How many of Tottenham's starting eleven were English?

435. Which German midfielder played for Tottenham in the final?

436. In what month of the year was the final played at Wembley?

437. What was the League Cup known as when Spurs won the Cup in 1999 - Worthington Cup, Coca-Cola Cup or Carling Cup?

438. What was the attendance at the final played at Wembley - 77,892, 78,892 or 79,892?

439. Which Swiss defender wore the number 15 shirt for Spurs in the final?

440. Which London team did Spurs beat 1-0 on aggregate in the semi-finals?

DARREN ANDERTON

441. From which team did Darren join Spurs in 1992?

442. How many League goals did Darren score for Spurs in his first season at The Lane, during the 1992/93 season?

443. What was the only trophy that Spurs won whilst Darren was a Tottenham player?

444. How many League appearances did Darren make for Spurs in his career - 299, 319 or 339?

445. Against which team did Darren score his first Tottenham goal, in the 57th minute, in a 4-2 home League win during February 1993?

446. Against which Yorkshire team did Darren score a Spurs brace in a 3-1 away League win during May 1996?

447. Darren made his Spurs League debut in a 0-0 away draw during August 1992, in Tottenham's first ever Premier League match, against which team?

448. True or false: Darren scored 22 League goals for Spurs in his football career?

449. What is Darren's middle name – Robert, Roger or Ryan?

450. How many goals did Darren score for England in his 30 full international caps?

MARK FALCO

451. How many League appearances did Mark make for Spurs in his career - 174, 184 or 194?

452. Which Spurs manager handed Mark his Tottenham League debut, at the age of 18?

453. How many League goals did Mark score for Spurs in his 42 appearances during the 1984/85 season – 20, 22 or 24?

454. True or false: Mark was voted as one of the top 50 greatest Spurs players of all time in 2009?

455. In what position did Mark play during his playing days?

456. In which year was Mark born in London – 1958, 1959 or 1960?

457. How many League goals did Mark score for Tottenham in his career – 68, 78 or 88?

458. Against which team did Mark make his Spurs debut, in a 3-1 win away from home during May 1979?

459. What was the only winners' medal that Mark won in his professional playing career for Spurs?

460. For which team did Mark sign when he left The Lane in 1986?

PAUL STEWART

461. With which team did Paul start his football career, turning professional in 1981?

462. True or false: Paul scored Tottenham's first goal in the 2-1 FA Cup final win in May 1991?

463. From which club did Paul sign when he arrived at White Hart Lane during June 1988?

464. How many League goals did Paul score for Spurs during his career – 26, 28 or 30?

465. Which manager signed Paul for Tottenham in June 1988?

466. Against which team did Paul make his Spurs debut, in a 2-2 home draw during October 1988?

467. What is Paul's middle name – Andrew, Adrian or Adam?

468. How many League games did Paul play for Tottenham during his playing career – 131, 331 or 531?

469. True or false: Paul won full international caps for England during his playing career at Tottenham?

470. For which team did Paul sign when he left White Hart Lane in 1992?

PETER SHREEVES

471. True or false: Peter was Spurs' youth team manager, reserve team boss and assistant manager before taking over from Keith Burkinshaw as Tottenham manager?

472. In which year was Peter born in Neath, Wales – 1938, 1939 or 1940?

473. To what position did Peter guide Tottenham in his first League season in charge at White Hart Lane?

474. Which manager took over at Spurs when Peter left in 1986?

475. In which season during the 1990s did Peter manage Spurs?

476. True or false: Peter played professional football for Spurs during his playing career?

477. Peter was Glenn Hoddle's assistant manager at which London club between 1993 and 1996?

478. True or false: Peter managed the England national team for two matches during the 1990s?

479. In which position did Peter play during his playing days – central defender, central midfielder or inside forward?

480. How many managerial spells did Peter have at Spurs?

PAUL GASCOIGNE

481. How many League goals did Paul score for Tottenham in his career – 18, 19 or 20?

482. From which club did Tottenham sign Paul in 1988?

483. In what year did Paul leave The Lane for Italian team Lazio?

484. True or false: Paul won the BBC Sports Personality of the Year award whilst at Tottenham Hotspur, in 1990?

485. How many League goals did Paul score for Spurs in his first season at the club, during the 1988/89 season?

486. What was the only winners' medal that Paul won whilst a Spurs player?

487. In 2005 Paul had a brief spell as manager of which team, a position that lasted 39 days?

488. How many League appearances did Paul make for Tottenham in his career – 82, 92 or 102?

489. What is Paul's middle name – John, Jeremy or Justin?

490. In what position did Paul play during his playing days?

2003/2004

491. Which Spurs striker scored a hat-trick against Wolves in a 5-2 home League win during December 2003?

492. With which League team did Tottenham draw 4-4 at home during February 2004?

493. Which team did Tottenham beat 2-0 away on the last day of the League season, with Robbie Keane and Jermain Defoe scoring Spurs' goals?

494. How many of their 38 League games did the club win during this season - 13, 15 or 17?

495. Who took over as caretaker manager for the remainder of the season when Glenn Hoddle left The Lane in September 2003?

496. Which midfielder scored Tottenham's winner in a 4-3 home League win against Portsmouth during February 2004?

497. How many League goals did Robbie Keane score for Tottenham during this season, finishing as the club's top scorer?

498. Which goalkeeper played in all 38 League games during this season?

499. Can you name the midfielder that signed for Spurs during January 2004 from Sheffield United?

500. Which French midfielder, on loan from Inter Milan, scored a brace in Spurs' 4-1 home League win against Birmingham during January 2004?

RICKY VILLA

501.   How many League goals did Ricky score for Tottenham
        in his career – 18, 22 or 26?

502.   In which year was Ricky born – 1950, 1951 or 1952?

503.   Which two winners' medals did Ricky win whilst a
        Spurs player?

504.   In what position did Ricky play during his playing
        days?

505.   Which manager signed Ricky for Tottenham?

506.   What nationality is Ricky?

507.   In what year did Ricky win the World Cup with his
        country?

508.   In what season did Ricky score seven League goals for
        Spurs, his best League tally of his White Hart Lane
        career?

509.   Against which team did Ricky make his goalscoring
        Spurs debut, in a 1-1 away draw during August 1978?

510.   How many League appearances did Ricky make for
        Tottenham in his career - 130, 133 or 136?

CHRIS WADDLE

511. How many League goals did Chris score for Tottenham in his playing career – 33, 44 or 55?

512. For which Premier League team did Chris play between 1992 and 1996?

513. In which year was Chris born in Felling, Tyne & Wear – 1958, 1959 or 1960?

514. For which French club did Chris sign when he left Spurs in 1989?

515. How many goals did Chris score for England in his 62 full international appearances?

516. What is Chris's middle name – Ralph, Roland or Rodney?

517. Against which team did Chris play on his Spurs League debut, on the opening day of the 1985/86 season, in a 4-0 home win, with Chris scoring twice in the game?

518. How many League appearances did Chris make for Tottenham in his playing career at White Hart Lane - 118, 128 or 138?

519. From which team did Chris sign for Spurs in 1985?

520. How many League goals did Chris score for Spurs during the 1988/89 season, his highest tally in a League season whilst a Spurs player?

PAUL WALSH

521. In which year was Paul born in Plumstead, London –
1961, 1962 or 1963?

522. Against which team did Paul make his Spurs debut, in
a 1-1 away draw during February 1988?

523. From which club did Paul sign when he joined Spurs in
1988 for £500,000?

524. How many League goals did Paul score for Spurs in his
career – 19, 29 or 39?

525. True or false: Paul was a Chelsea fan as a young boy?

526. What was the only winners' medal that Paul won
during his Spurs career?

527. In what position did Paul play during his playing days?

528. True or false: Paul won full international caps for
England during his playing career?

529. For which team did Paul sign when he left The Lane in
1992?

530. How many League appearances did Paul make for
Spurs in his career – 118, 128 or 138?

CHRISTIAN ZIEGE

531.   What nationality is Christian?

532.   In what year did Spurs sign Christian from Liverpool?

533.   True or false: Christian was the first ever player with a surname beginning with 'Z' to play for Spurs?

534.   How many League goals did Christian score for Tottenham in his career – 3, 5 or 7?

535.   Against which London team did Christian score Tottenham's League goal after 11 minutes in a 1-1 draw at White Hart Lane during December 2002?

536.   For which English team did Christian play during the 1999/2000 season?

537.   How many League goals did Christian score for Spurs in his first season at the club?

538.   True or false: Christian scored Tottenham's goal in the 2-1 defeat against Blackburn Rovers in the League Cup final in February 2002?

539.   Which Spurs manager signed Christian to bring him to The Lane?

540.   How many League appearances did Christian make for Spurs in his career – 43, 45 or 47?

2002/2003

541. Which Spurs striker scored a hat-trick in a 4-3 home League win against Everton during January 2003?

542. True or false: Spurs conceded nine goals in the final two games of the League season?

543. What was the score when Leeds United visited White Hart Lane in a League match during November 2002?

544. With which team did Spurs draw 2-2 at home on Boxing Day 2002, having been 2-0 down after 49 minutes?

545. Can you name the Spurs strike partnership that scored 25 League goals between them during this season?

546. Which goalkeeper played in all 38 League games during this season – Paul Robinson, Kasey Keller or Ian Walker?

547. How many League goals did Simon Davies score for Tottenham during this season – 5, 6 or 7?

548. Which Spurs midfielder scored the winning goal in a 2-1 home win against Birmingham City during April 2003?

549. Tottenham finished 10th in the League, a higher placing than which three other London clubs?

550. Which Tottenham striker scored the winning goal in the 85th minute in a 3-2 away win against West Bromwich Albion during April 2003?

UEFA CUP WINNERS - 1984

551. Which player scored for Spurs in the 1-1 away draw in the 1st leg in the UEFA Cup final?

552. Can you name seven of Tottenham's starting eleven in the 2nd leg, with Spurs drawing 1-1 at White Hart Lane before winning 4-3 on penalties?

553. Which Spurs manager guided the club to this success?

554. Which player scored for Tottenham in the 1-1 home draw in the 2nd leg?

555. In what month of the year were both the 1st and 2nd legs of the final played?

556. What was the attendance in the final 2nd leg, played at White Hart Lane - 46,258, 48,258 or 50,258?

557. Which Yugoslavian team did Spurs beat 2-2 on away goals in the UEFA Cup semi-finals?

558. Can you name the two Spurs goalscorers when Tottenham beat Bayern Munich 2-0 at home in the 3rd round, 2nd leg?

559. Can you name two of the four players that scored Tottenham's four penalties in the final 2nd leg, winning the competition against Anderlecht in the final?

560. Who captained Spurs in the final 2nd leg, after Steve Perryman captained in the final 1st leg?

GERRY FRANCIS

561.   In what year was Gerry appointed as Spurs boss, his
       first game in charge being a 4-3 home defeat to Aston
       Villa on the day that the first ever national lottery
       draw took place?

562.   To what position in the League did Gerry guide
       Tottenham during the 1996/97 season?

563.   Which midfielder did Gerry sign from Newcastle
       United during July 1997?

564.   Which team did Gerry manage between 1987 and
       1991?

565.   Who took over as Tottenham manager at White Hart
       Lane when Gerry left in November 1997?

566.   True or false: Gerry played for Tottenham during his
       playing days?

567.   In which year was Gerry born in London – 1951, 1952
       or 1953?

568.   Which team did Gerry manage before taking charge at
       White Hart Lane?

569.   To which round did Gerry guide Tottenham in the 1995
       FA Cup?

570.   To what position in the League did Gerry guide Spurs
       in his first season in charge at The Lane?

GLENN HODDLE

571. How many League goals did Glenn score for Spurs in his career – 66, 77 or 88?

572. In what year was Glenn appointed as Spurs manager?

573. What was the name of the single that Glenn released with another former Spurs player, Chris Waddle, in 1987?

574. How many League appearances did Glenn make for Tottenham during his career - 317, 347 or 377?

575. Which Spurs manager handed Glenn his Spurs debut, against Norwich City during August 1975?

576. For which French team did Glenn sign when he left The Lane in 1987?

577. True or false: Glenn scored 19 League goals for Spurs during the 1979/80 season?

578. How many times did Glenn win an FA Cup winners' medal whilst a Spurs player?

579. In which year was Glenn born in Hayes, Middlesex – 1956, 1957 or 1958?

580. Which team did Glenn manage between 1996 and 1999?

CHRIS HUGHTON

581. In what position did Chris play during his playing days?

582. How many full international caps did Chris win for the Republic of Ireland – 43, 53 or 63?

583. How many times did Chris win the FA Cup whilst a Spurs player?

584. How many League goals did Chris score for Spurs during the 1982/83 season?

585. For which London team did Chris sign when he left White Hart Lane in 1990?

586. For which team was Chris appointed manager in 2009?

587. How many League goals did Chris score for Spurs in his career - 12, 14 or 16?

588. Against which team did Chris make his Tottenham debut, in a 2-1 home win during September 1979?

589. In which year was Chris born in London – 1957, 1958 or 1959?

590. How many League appearances did Chris make for Spurs in his career - 293, 295 or 297?

2001/2002

591.   Which defender did Tottenham purchase from Southampton for over £8 million during September 2001?

592.   Can you name the two Spurs players that finished the League season with 10 goals apiece?

593.   Which goalkeeper started 29 League matches during this season?

594.   Which midfielder scored the club's equaliser in the 90th minute in a 1-1 home draw with Arsenal during November 2001?

595.   How many of their 38 League matches did Tottenham win - 14, 15 or 16?

596.   Which goalkeeper did Tottenham sign from Rayo Vallecano during August 2001?

597.   Who was manager of Tottenham during this season, his first full season in charge at White Hart Lane?

598.   Which midfielder scored Spurs' only goal in a 1-0 home win over Liverpool during April 2002?

599.   Which team beat Spurs 5-3 at home during September 2001, Spurs having been 3-0 up at half-time?

600.   How many League goals did Les Ferdinand score for Spurs during this season – 7, 8 or 9?

TOM HUDDLESTONE

601. From which team did Tom sign for Tottenham during 2005?

602. Which England manager handed Tom his full England debut in 2009?

603. How many League goals did Tom score for Spurs during the 2007/08 season – 2, 3 or 4?

604. In which year was Tom born in Nottingham – 1984, 1985 or 1986?

605. Which Spurs manager signed Tom for the club?

606. What is Tom's middle name – Andrew, Aaron or Anthony?

607. Against which club did Tom score Tottenham's second goal in a 2-0 home League win during November 2009?

608. True or false: Tom scored the club's only goal in a 1-0 home League win against Bolton Wanderers during May 2010?

609. Against which team did Tom score a brace for Spurs, in the 80th and 99th minutes, in a 3-1 home win (after extra time) in the League Cup 4th round during November 2006?

610. True or false: Tom scored twice for Tottenham, both times in the UEFA Cup, during the 2008/09 season?

DAVID HOWELLS

611. How many League goals did David score for Spurs in the first Premier League season, during 1992/93?

612. In which year was David born in Guildford – 1965, 1967 or 1969?

613. True or false: David scored on his Tottenham League debut, in a 2-1 win at Sheffield Wednesday during February 1986?

614. How many League games did David play for Spurs in his playing career - 277, 287 or 297?

615. What nationality is David – Welsh, Scottish or English?

616. How many League goals did David score for Tottenham in his playing career – 18, 20 or 22?

617. For which club did David sign when he left The Lane in 1998?

618. In what position did David play during his playing days?

619. David scored for Spurs against which two teams during the 1996/97 season?

620. Which Spurs manager handed David his Tottenham League debut?

FA CUP WINNERS - 1981

621. Which Spurs midfielder scored a brace for Spurs in a 3-2 win in the FA Cup final replay?

622. Which team did Spurs beat in the FA Cup final replay?

623. Which player for the opposition scored for his own team and also scored Spurs' equaliser in the 79th minute in the FA Cup final?

624. Can you name Spurs' goalkeeper in the FA Cup final and FA Cup final replay?

625. Which Tottenham manager guided the club to this success?

626. What was the name of Tottenham's Cup final song, recorded by the musical duo Chas and Dave?

627. Can you name seven of Tottenham's starting eleven in the FA Cup final replay?

628. True or false: the year of 1981 marked the 100th FA Cup final in history?

629. What was the score at half-time in the FA Cup final replay, with the game finishing 3-2 to Tottenham?

630. Was this the 5th, 6th or 7th time that Spurs had won the FA Cup in their history?

2000/2001

631. Which defender did Spurs purchase from Wimbledon for £5 million during July 2000?

632. How many League goals did Sergei Rebrov score during this season, his first season at The Lane?

633. Ian Walker played in goal three games this season, but which goalkeeper played in the other 35 League games?

634. Which Tottenham midfielder scored the club's winner in the 41st minute in a 2-1 home win against Liverpool during November 2000?

635. Which team did Tottenham beat 3-0 at home, with Steffen Iversen, Les Ferdinand and Sergei Rebrov scoring the goals, during March 2001?

636. Which Tottenham defender scored a brace, including an 88th-minute winner, away at Sunderland in a 3-2 win during April 2001?

637. Which Dutch midfielder scored a Tottenham brace in a 3-1 home win against Manchester United during May 2001?

638. Which East Anglian team did Spurs beat 3-1 at home on the opening day of the League season during August 2000?

639. How many of their 19 away League games did Tottenham win – 2, 10 or 18?

640. Which forward finished as Tottenham's top League scorer this season, with ten goals?

LEAGUE HAT-TRICKS

Match up the League opponents with the player who scored a hat-trick for Spurs

641.   v. Leeds United,
     February 1993   **Jermain Defoe**

642.   v. Everton,
     December 1998   **Jermain Defoe**

643.   v. Everton,   **Teddy**
     January 2003   **Sheringham**

644.   v. Wigan Athletic,
     November 2009   **Les Ferdinand**

645.   v. Sunderland,   **Jürgen**
     March 1997   **Klinsmann**

646.   v. Wimbledon,   **Teddy**
     May 1998   **Sheringham**

647.   v. Southampton,
     December 2004   **Robbie Keane**

648.   v. Leicester City,
     November 2000   **Jermain Defoe**

649.   v. Hull City,
     August 2009   **Chris Armstrong**

650.   v. Newcastle United,
     December 1994   **Steffen Iversen**

TIM SHERWOOD

651. How many League goals did Tim score for Spurs in his football career – 10, 12 or 14?

652. From which team did Tim sign when he arrived at White Hart Lane in 1999?

653. Against which team did Tim make his Spurs League debut, in a 0-0 home draw during February 1999?

654. True or false: Tim made his full England debut at the age of 35?

655. In which year was Tim born in St Albans – 1967, 1968 or 1969?

656. Against which team did Tim score a Spurs brace in a 4-0 home League win on Boxing Day 1999?

657. In what position did Tim play during his playing days – left back, central midfielder or striker?

658. Against which team did Tim score Spurs' second and winning goal in a 2-1 home League win during November 1999?

659. Which Spurs manager signed Tim for Tottenham in 1999?

660. How many League appearances did Tim make for Spurs in his career - 93, 153 or 193?

1999/2000

661. Which team did Spurs beat 7-2 at home during March 2000?

662. Following on from the previous question, which Spurs striker scored a hat-trick in the game?

663. Which forward scored the club's only goal in a 1-0 home win against Liverpool during January 2000?

664. What was the score when Sunderland visited White Hart Lane in May 2000, the last day of the League season?

665. Which team did Spurs beat 3-1 at home during August 1999, with Steffen Iversen, Les Ferdinand and Tim Sherwood scoring the goals?

666. Who was Spurs' boss during this season?

667. Can you name the two Spurs strikers that finished the season with 14 League goals?

668. Who was the only Tottenham player to play in all 38 League matches this season?

669. How many of their 38 League matches did the club win during this season – 15, 17 or 19?

670. True or false: Spurs were unbeaten in the four League matches played in January 2000?

JERMAINE JENAS

671.   From which club did Jermaine sign when he joined
       Spurs in August 2005?

672.   Against which club did Jermaine make his Spurs debut,
       in a 0-0 home League draw in September 2005?

673.   Against which club did Jermaine score his first
       Tottenham League goal, in a 2-0 home win during
       October 2005?

674.   What is Jermaine's middle name – Anthony, Adrian or
       Arthur?

675.   Against which country did Jermaine score his first
       England international goal, in a 2-1 England win
       during February 2008?

676.   How many League goals did Jermaine score for
       Tottenham in his first season at the club, during the
       2005/06 season?

677.   Against which team did Jermaine score his only League
       goal of the 2009/10 season, in a 5-0 home win during
       September 2009?

678.   In which year was Jermaine born in Nottingham –
       1981, 1982 or 1983?

679.   Against which Midlands team did Jermaine score
       Spurs' only goal in a 1-0 home League win during May
       2009?

680.   At which club did Jermaine start his professional
       football career?

KEITH BURKINSHAW

681. How many times did Keith guide Spurs to win the FA Cup during his managerial career?

682. True or false: Keith played for Spurs during his playing career?

683. Although he is known by the name Keith, this is his middle name. What is his real first name?

684. In which year did Keith leave The Lane, with Peter Shreeves taking over as Spurs' boss?

685. What was the last Cup that Spurs won whilst Keith was the Tottenham manager?

686. In which position did Keith play during his playing days – defender, midfielder or striker?

687. Which English team did Keith manage during the 1993/94 season?

688. In which year was Keith born in Barnsley – 1933, 1935 or 1937?

689. Who was Tottenham's manager before Keith took charge at The Lane in 1976?

690. True or false: Keith is Tottenham's second most successful manager in the club's history behind Bill Nicholson?

ROBBIE KEANE

691. Against which London team did Robbie make his Spurs debut, in a 3-2 home win during September 2002, with Simon Davies, Teddy Sheringham and Anthony Gardner scoring Tottenham's goals?

692. Against which team did Robbie score a Tottenham hat-trick in a 4-3 home League win during January 2003?

693. Against which team did Robbie score a Spurs brace in a 4-1 home League win during February 2007, with Jermaine Jenas and Aaron Lennon scoring the other goals?

694. Against which team did Robbie score four goals for Spurs in a 5-0 home win in the Premier League during September 2009?

695. How many League goals did Robbie score for Tottenham during the 2005/06 season – 14, 16 or 18?

696. For which country is Robbie a full international?

697. For which Italian team did Robbie play during the 2000/01 season?

698. For which team did Robbie sign when he left The Lane in 2008, only to return to Tottenham in 2009?

699. Which Tottenham manager signed Robbie for his first spell at the club?

700. In which year was Robbie born in Dublin – 1978, 1979 or 1980?

JUANDE RAMOS

701. Which team did Spurs beat 2-0 in the League Cup 4th round in Juande's first match in charge at Tottenham during October 2007?

702. Following on from the previous question, can you name the two Spurs scorers in the game?

703. How many of their 54 League matches did the club win under Juande – 18, 21 or 24?

704. True or false: Juande retired from playing football at the age of 28 due to a knee injury?

705. Which Spanish team did Juande manage before he was appointed as Spurs' boss?

706. To which position did Juande guide Tottenham in the Premier League during the 2007/08 season – 9th,10th or 11th?

707. In which year was Juande born – 1953, 1954 or 1955?

708. In what position did Juande play during his playing days?

709. Which Cup did Juande win as Spurs' manager during his time at the club?

710. Which Spanish giants did Juande go on to manage when he left Spurs, during the 2008/09 season?

1998/1999

711. How many of their League matches did the club win during this season – 11, 13 or 15?

712. Which defender left The Lane for Aston Villa during March 1999?

713. Which striker scored nine League goals, finishing as Tottenham's highest League scorer this season?

714. Which forward scored the only goal in Spurs' third League match and first League win of the season, a 1-0 away win against Everton during August 1998?

715. What was the score when Tottenham visited Charlton Athletic during April 1999?

716. Can you name Spurs' two goalscorers in a 2-2 home draw with Chelsea in the League during May 1999?

717. Which defender scored Tottenham's 90th-minute equaliser in a 3-3 home League draw against Leeds United during September 1998?

718. Who started the season as Tottenham manager?

719. Which defender scored a brace, including Tottenham's 90th-minute equaliser, in a 2-2 home League draw against Manchester United during December 1998?

720. Which defender signed for Spurs from Ipswich Town during November 1998?

LEDLEY KING

721. What is Ledley's middle name – Brenton, Brendan or Breedon?

722. Which squad number did Ledley wear during the 2010/11 season?

723. Against which country did Ledley play for England for 45 minutes in their first game of the 2010 World Cup, the game ending in a 1-1 draw, with Steven Gerrard scoring England's goal?

724. Which manager handed Ledley his Tottenham League debut in 1999?

725. Against which team did Ledley score his first goal for Tottenham, in a 3-3 draw during December 2000, setting a new Premier League record for the quickest goal scored in a game at just 10.2 seconds?

726. Against which team did Ledley make his League debut for Spurs, in a 3-2 away defeat during May 1999?

727. In what position does Ledley play?

728. True or false: Ledley won the Premier League Player of the Month award during September 2004?

729. Against which country did Ledley score for England in a 3-1 win at Wembley in a friendly match during May 2010?

730. In which year was Ledley born in London – 1979, 1980 or 1981?

AARON LENNON

731. From which club did Aaron sign for Spurs in 2005?

732. True or false: Aaron won Tottenham's Player of the Year and Young Player of the Year awards at the end of the 2008/09 season?

733. How many League goals did Aaron score for Spurs during the 2008/09 season – 3, 5 or 7?

734. Against which London team did Aaron make his Spurs debut, in a 2-0 home defeat during August 2005?

735. Against which Midlands team did Aaron score his first Spurs goal, in a 2-0 away League win during March 2006?

736. Against which two countries did Aaron play for England in the 2010 World Cup in South Africa?

737. What squad number did Aaron wear for Spurs during the 2010/11 season?

738. What was the transfer free when Aaron joined Tottenham?

739. What is Aaron's middle name – Jamie, Justin or Jonathan?

740. Against which London team did Aaron score Tottenham's winner in the 52nd minute in a 2-1 home League win during November 2006?

1997/1998

741. Can you name the three Spurs goalscorers in Tottenham's 3-3 League home draw against Liverpool during March 1998?

742. Which Spurs midfielder scored in the 28th minute against Arsenal in a 1-1 League draw at The Lane during December 1997?

743. Which Italian midfielder did Tottenham sign from Inter Milan during January 1998?

744. True or false: Spurs were unbeaten in the five League matches played during April 1998?

745. Against which club did Spurs record their first League win of the season, during August 1997, with Colin Calderwood scoring the only goal in the game, after defeats to Manchester United (at home) and West Ham United (away)?

746. In which position did Spurs finish in the League – 12th, 14th or 16th?

747. Which Tottenham striker finished as the club's highest League scorer with 9 goals in 15 matches?

748. Who started the season as Spurs' boss before Christian Gross took charge in November 1997?

749. Which winger did Spurs sign from Sporting Lisbon during August 1997?

750. Which striker scored Tottenham's only goal in a 1-0 home League win against West Ham United during January 1998?

GARY LINEKER

751. How many League goals did Gary score for Tottenham in his career – 65, 66 or 67?

752. In what year did Gary sign for Spurs from Barcelona?

753. True or false: Gary scored 28 League goals in 35 matches for Spurs during the 1991/92 season?

754. Against which country did Gary score his first England hat-trick, in a World Cup qualifier 5-0 win at Wembley Stadium during October 1985?

755. Where in England was Gary born in 1960 – Leeds, Leicester or London?

756. For which English team did Gary play during the 1985/86 season, finishing the season with 30 League goals, his best ever tally in a League season in his professional career?

757. How many goals did Gary score for England in his career – 47, 48 or 49?

758. What is Gary's middle name – Winston, Wilfred or William?

759. In how many League games did Gary play for Spurs in his football career – 85, 95 or 105?

760. For which Japanese team did Gary sign when he left The Lane in 1992?

GARY MABBUTT

761. How many League goals did Gary score for Tottenham in his career, in 458 starts and 19 substitute appearances – 23, 25 or 27?

762. In what year did Gary make his final Spurs appearance, in a 1-1 home League draw against Southampton?

763. Against which team did Gary score Tottenham's winning goal in a 2-1 home win in the Premier League during December 1992?

764. True or false: Gary scored for both sides in the Spurs v. Coventry City FA Cup final in 1987, which ended in a 3-2 Tottenham defeat?

765. Can you recall the name of either Gary's father or his brother, both former professional footballers?

766. From which club did Gary sign for Spurs in 1982?

767. What trophy did Gary lift as Spurs captain in 1991?

768. How many full international England caps did Gary win during his playing career, scoring one goal for his country – 15, 16 or 17?

769. In what position did Gary play during his playing days?

770. In which year was Gary born in Bristol – 1961, 1963 or 1965?

NAYIM

771. From which Spanish team did Spurs sign Nayim in the late 1980s?

772. How many League games did Nayim play for Spurs in his football career – 102, 112 or 122?

773. Which Spurs manager sign Nayim for Tottenham?

774. Against which East Anglian team did Nayim score Spurs' fifth goal in a 5-1 home League win during April 1993?

775. In what position did Nayim play – defender, midfielder or striker?

776. True or false: Nayim represented Spain at under 18, under 19, under 20 and under 21 level?

777. Against which club did Nayim score a Spurs hat-trick in a 4-2 FA Cup away win in 1993?

778. How many League goals did Nayim score for Spurs in his football career – 9, 11 or 13?

779. Which winners' medal did Nayim pick up during his time at Tottenham?

780. For which Spanish team did Nayim sign in 1993 when he left White Hart Lane?

GEORGE GRAHAM

781. George was in charge at which club in between his management spells at Arsenal and Tottenham?

782. Which Cup did George win for Tottenham in his first season in charge at White Hart Lane?

783. In which year was George born in Glasgow – 1942, 1943 or 1944?

784. To what position in the League did George guide Spurs during his first season in charge?

785. Which striker did George sign for Spurs from Dynamo Kiev during June 2000?

786. Which midfielder did George sign from Blackburn Rovers for £4 million during February 1999?

787. What percentage of games did George win as Spurs manager – 39%, 42% or 45%?

788. To what position in the League did George guide Spurs during the 1999/2000 season?

789. For which country did George win 12 international caps, scoring 3 goals, in his career?

790. In what year was George sacked as Tottenham manager?

1996/1997

791. How many League goals did Teddy Sheringham score for Spurs during this season – 7, 8 or 9?

792. Goalkeeper Ian Walker started 37 of Spurs' 38 League matches this season, but who took his place in goal in the game he missed?

793. Which team did Tottenham beat 3-1 at The Lane on Boxing Day 1996, with Steffen Iversen scoring a brace and Allan Nielsen scoring the other Spurs goal?

794. True or false: Tottenham were unbeaten in their three League matches played during February 1997?

795. Which Tottenham striker scored a hat-trick away at Sunderland in a 4-0 League win during March 1997?

796. Who managed Spurs during this season, his last full season in charge at The Lane?

797. How many of their 38 League matches did the club win during this season - 13, 14 or 15?

798. Which defender signed for Spurs from Liverpool during December 1996?

799. Can you name the only Spurs player to play in all 38 League matches during this season?

800. Which team beat Spurs 7-1 away from home during December 1996?

ROMAN PAVLYUCHENKO

801. What nationality is Roman?

802. How many League goals did Roman score for Spurs in his first season at The Lane, during the 2008/09 season?

803. Against which team did Roman make his Spurs debut, in a 2-1 home defeat during September 2008?

804. Against which team did Roman score a brace in a 4-0 home win in an FA Cup 5th round replay during February 2010?

805. What squad number did Roman wear during the 2010/11 season?

806. In what position does Roman play?

807. Against which team did Roman score his first Spurs goal, in the 62nd minute of a 2-1 away win in the League Cup 3rd round during September 2008?

808. Against which Lancashire team did Roman score a Spurs League brace in a 3-1 home win during March 2010, with Jermain Defoe scoring the other Tottenham goal?

809. In which year was Roman born – 1980, 1981 or 1982?

810. From which Russian team did Roman sign for Spurs in 2008?

FA CUP WINNERS - 1982

811. Which goalkeeper played in both the FA Cup final and FA Cup final replay for Spurs?

812. What was the score in the FA Cup final replay, after drawing the final 1-1 at Wembley?

813. Which London team did Spurs beat in the FA Cup final replay?

814. Can you name the three non-English players that played for Spurs in the FA Cup final and FA Cup final replay?

815. Which team did Spurs beat in the FA Cup semi-final?

816. Was this victory Spurs' 7th, 8th or 9th FA Cup win in their history?

817. True or false: Spurs went into the FA Cup final as holders of the trophy?

818. Who was Tottenham's captain during this success?

819. Which Tottenham player scored in both the FA Cup final and FA Cup final replay?

820. Which Spurs manager guided the club to this success?

STEVE PERRYMAN

821. In which year was Steve born in London - 1951, 1953 or 1955?

822. Against which team did Steve make his Spurs debut, in a 1-0 defeat at home during September 1969?

823. How many League goals did Steve score for Spurs during the 1980/81 season – 2, 4 or 6?

824. How old was Steve when he became Spurs' captain?

825. How many times did Steve win the FA Cup whilst a Spurs player?

826. How many League appearances did Steve make for Spurs during his playing career - 655, 705 or 755?

827. For which team did Steve sign when he left White Hart Lane in 1986?

828. Against which country did Steve win his only full England cap, as a substitute during June 1982?

829. In what year did Steve win the Football Writers' Association Footballer of the Year award?

830. How many League goals did Steve score for Tottenham in his football career - 31, 41 or 51?

1995/1996

831.   Can you name two of the three Spurs goalscorers in the club's 3-2 away League win against Coventry City during November 1995?

832.   Which Tottenham striker scored the club's winner in a 2-1 home League win against Arsenal during November 1995?

833.   Which team finished higher in the League – Tottenham or Chelsea?

834.   What was the score when Tottenham visited Southampton at The Dell on Boxing Day 1995?

835.   How many of their 38 League matches did the club win - 16, 17 or 18?

836.   Which Spurs striker scored a brace in the club's 4-1 home League win against Manchester United on New Year's Day 1996?

837.   Who was Spurs' boss during this season?

838.   Which midfielder left White Hart Lane for Reading during February 1996?

839.   Against which team did Spurs record their first League win of the season, a 2-1 home win in their fifth League game during September 1995?

840.   Which Spurs player scored a brace in a 3-1 away League win against Leeds United during May 1996?

GUS POYET

841. From which London team did Gus sign when he came to The Lane in 2001?

842. In what position did Gus play - defender, midfielder or striker?

843. For which country was Gus a full international during his playing days?

844. How many League appearances did Gus make for Tottenham in his football career – 80, 82 or 84?

845. Which Spurs manager signed Gus in June 2001?

846. Against which team did Gus score a brace for Spurs in a 4-0 home win in the FA Cup 5th round during February 2002?

847. For which Spanish team did Gus play between 1990 and 1997?

848. Against which team did Gus score Tottenham's winner, in the 89th minute, in a 4-3 home League win during February 2004?

849. Gus became manager of which English club in 2009?

850. How many League goals did Gus score for Tottenham in his career – 16, 18 or 20?

MARTIN JOL

851.   In what year was Martin appointed as Spurs manager?

852.   When Martin first arrived at White Hart Lane he took up the position of assistant to which Spurs manager?

853.   True or false: Martin won the Manager of the Month award in only his second month in charge of Tottenham?

854.   In which year was Martin born in The Netherlands – 1956, 1957 or 1958?

855.   To what position did Martin guide Spurs during the 2006/07 season, securing UEFA Cup qualification on the final day of the season and making him the first Spurs manager since Keith Burkinshaw to qualify for European football in successive seasons?

856.   In which position did Martin play during his playing days – defender, midfielder or striker?

857.   For which two English teams did Martin play during his playing days, the first from 1982 to 1984 and the second from 1984 to 1985?

858.   Martin was appointed as manager of which Dutch side in 2009?

859.   Who took over from Martin as boss at The Lane during October 2007?

860.   True or false: Martin was a full international for his country during his playing days?

1994/1995

861. Which team did Spurs beat 4-3 away from home on the opening day of the League season, with Darren Anderton, Nick Barmby, Jürgen Klinsmann and Teddy Sheringham scoring the goals for Tottenham during August 1994?

862. Who started the season as Tottenham manager?

863. Which midfielder did Tottenham purchase from PSV Eindhoven for £2.9 million during September 1994?

864. Can you name Tottenham's two goalscorers in the 2-0 away win against Norwich City on Boxing Day 1994?

865. What was the score when Tottenham played Coventry City away from home on New Year's Eve 1994?

866. Which striker scored Tottenham's goal at Highbury when Spurs and Arsenal drew 1-1 in the League during April 1995?

867. Which team finished highest in the League – Tottenham, Chelsea or Arsenal?

868. Which Tottenham defender left White Hart Lane for Bolton Wanderers during March 1995?

869. Which forward scored a League hat-trick for Spurs in a 4-2 home win over Newcastle United during December 1994?

870. Which team beat Spurs 4-3 at White Hart Lane during November 1994, in Gerry Francis's first League game in charge at the club?

GRAHAM ROBERTS

871. How many League appearances did Graham make for Tottenham during his Spurs career - 209, 309 or 409?

872. True or false: Graham won full international caps for England during his playing career?

873. Can you name the three winners' medals that Graham won whilst a Spurs player?

874. For which London team did Graham play between 1988 and 1990?

875. In what position did Graham play during his playing days?

876. What is Graham's middle name – Paul, Peter or Philip?

877. What is the name of Graham's 2008 autobiography?

878. For which team did Graham sign when he left White Hart Lane in 1986?

879. How many League goals did Graham score for Spurs in his career – 13, 23 or 33?

880. Against which team did Graham make his Tottenham League debut, in a 3-2 away win during October 1980?

1993/1994

881.   Which Spurs striker scored the only goal on the opening day of the League season, in a 1-0 away win against Newcastle United?

882.   Can you name the Spurs League goalscorers in a 3-3 home draw against Liverpool during December 1993?

883.   How many of their 42 League matches did the club win - 11, 13 or 15?

884.   Which striker did Tottenham sign from Liverpool during January 1994?

885.   Which team did Spurs beat 5-0 at home in the League during September 1993, with Teddy Sheringham scoring a brace in the game?

886.   True or false: Spurs lost all four League matches during January 1994?

887.   Which fullback signed for Tottenham from Leeds United during September 1993?

888.   Which team did Spurs beat 3-0 at home in the League during April 1994, with Darren Anderton, Vinny Samways and Steve Sedgley scoring the goals?

889.   Can you name Tottenham's two scorers in a 2-2 away League draw with Sheffield United during September 1993?

890.   Which striker left White Hart Lane for Rangers during November 1993?

PAUL ROBINSON

891. How many League appearances did Paul make for Spurs in his career – 127, 137 or 147?

892. In what year did Paul join Tottenham?

893. From which Yorkshire team did Paul sign when he arrived at The Lane?

894. Against which team did Paul score Tottenham's second goal in the 63rd minute of a 3-1 home League win during March 2007?

895. What was the only winners' medal that Paul won at Tottenham during his career?

896. How many full international caps did Paul win for England during his playing career – 21, 31 or 41?

897. True or false: Paul was ever present in League competition for Spurs during the 2005/06 and 2006/07 seasons?

898. How many League goals did Paul score for Tottenham in his career - 1, 2 or 3?

899. What is Paul's middle name – William, Wayne or Warren?

900. For which club did Paul sign when he left White Hart Lane in 2008?

VINNY SAMWAYS

901.   How many League appearances did Vinny make for Tottenham in his playing career - 193, 195 or 197?

902.   For which Premier League team did Vinny sign when he left The Lane in 1994?

903.   True or false: Vinny was in Tottenham's starting eleven in the 1991 FA Cup final against Nottingham Forest?

904.   In what position did Vinny play during his playing days?

905.   How many League goals did Vinny score for Spurs in the 1988/89 season - 3, 5 or 7?

906.   True or false: Vinny won a full international cap for England during his playing days?

907.   Against which team did Vinny make his Spurs debut, in a 2-1 defeat away during May 1987?

908.   In which year was Vinny born in London – 1967, 1968 or 1969?

909.   For which Midlands team did Vinny play during the 2003/04 season?

910.   How many League goals did Vinny score for Tottenham during his career – 11, 13 or 15?

DAVID PLEAT

911.   In which 1980s season did David manage Spurs?

912.   What is David's middle name – John, Joseph or James?

913.   To what position in the League did David guide Tottenham during his season as manager?

914.   True or false: David guided Tottenham to both the FA Cup final and the League Cup semi-finals during his season in charge of the club?

915.   Which team did David manage from 1978, prior to taking charge at Tottenham?

916.   In what year did David return to White Hart Lane as Director of Football?

917.   True or false: David once played a League match for Tottenham during his playing days?

918.   In what position did David play during his playing days?

919.   Which team did David manage between 1995 and 1997?

920.   In which year was David born in Nottingham – 1943, 1945 or 1947?

SQUAD NUMBERS – 2010/2011

*Match up the player with the squad number
they wore during the 2010/2011 season*

921.	Kyle Walker	8
922.	Younes Kaboul	25
923.	Wilson Palacios	39
924.	Roman Pavlyuchenko	1
925.	Heurelho Gomes	12
926.	Sébastien Bassong	4
927.	Danny Rose	28
928.	David Bentley	9
929.	Jonathan Woodgate	5
930.	Jermaine Jenas	19

WHITE HART LANE

931.   Tottenham's ground, White Hart Lane, is situated on the High Road in Tottenham, but can you recall the postcode?

932.   Against which team did Spurs play their first game, a friendly, at White Hart Lane, in a 4-1 win in front of a crowd of 5,000?

933.   In what year was the South Stand redeveloped, including the installation of the first giant Sony Jumbotron TV screen at the ground?

934.   True or false: White Hart Lane hosted American football in 1995 and 1996 as the home ground of the London Monarchs?

935.   What is the nearest tube station to White Hart Lane, a 1.4 mile walk to the stadium?

936.   Against which team did Spurs achieve their record home attendance of 75,038, in an FA Cup tie during March 1938?

937.   In which year did the club move to White Hart Lane – 1899, 1900 or 1901?

938.   Which stand is situated on Bill Nicholson Way?

939.   What are the dimensions of Tottenham's pitch – 95 metres x 62 metres, 100 metres x 67 metres or 105 metres x 72 metres?

940.   What is the name of the train station that is situated about a four-minute walk away from the stadium?

CLUB HISTORY

941.   In what year was the club formed?

942.   Which Dutch player signed for Spurs in August 2010 from Real Madrid?

943.   Which club did Spurs play in their first ever Champions League match, in the play-off first leg at White Hart Lane during August 2010, in a 3-2 away defeat?

944.   Can you name the three teams who were in Tottenham's group (group A) in the Champions League during the 2010/2011 season?

945.   In what year did Spurs first win the FA Cup?

946.   Who scored a hat-trick for Spurs in the Champions League play-off second leg in a 4-0 home win during August 2010?

947.   When Spurs won the League Cup in 2008, was this the 2nd, 3rd or 4th time the club had won this trophy in their history?

948.   Which team did Tottenham beat 9-0, to record their record League win, playing in the Second Division during October 1977?

949.   Which French defender signed for Spurs from Arsenal during August 2010?

950.   Who were the club's first ever shirt sponsors in their history?

LEAGUE APPEARANCES – 3

*Match up the player with the number of League
appearances he made for Spurs in his career*

951.	Timothée Atouba	91 (1)
952.	Young-Pyo Lee	10 (11)
953.	Micky Hazard	22 (1)
954.	Mark Bowen	17 (4)
955.	Paul Gascoigne	60
956.	Rory Allen	68 (2)
957.	Chris Fairclough	23 (10)
958.	Hossam Ghaly	88 (31)
959.	Espen Baardsen	14 (3)
960.	Andy Gray	15 (3)

SQUAD NUMBERS – 1994/1995

*Match up the player with the squad number
he wore during the 1994/95 season*

961.	Gheorghe Popescu	14
962.	Ian Walker	15
963.	Sol Campbell	3
964.	Ronny Rosenthal	7
965.	Justin Edinburgh	22
966.	Ilie Dumitrescu	13
967.	David Howells	8
968.	David Kerslake	4
969.	Nick Barmby	11
970.	Stuart Nethercott	23

LEAGUE APPEARANCES – 4

Match up the player with the number of League appearances he made for Spurs in his career

971.	Gerry Armstrong	12 (10)
972.	Dean Austin	28 (3)
973.	Matthew Etherington	61 (3)
974.	Ian Crook	152 (11)
975.	Ray Clemence	11 (4)
976.	Michael Carrick	20 (25)
977.	Colin Calderwood	65 (19)
978.	Stéphane Dalmat	240
979.	Edgar Davids	10 (10)
980.	Sean Davis	117 (7)

POSITIONS IN THE LEAGUE

Match up the season with the club's finishing position in Division One

981.	1980/81	13th in Division One
982.	1981/82	3rd in Division One
983.	1982/83	3rd in Division One
984.	1983/84	10th in Division One
985.	1984/85	10th in Division One
986.	1985/86	3rd in Division One
987.	1986/87	8th in Division One
988.	1987/88	4th in Division One
989.	1988/89	4th in Division One
990.	1989/90	6th in Division One

INTERNATIONALS

*Match up the player with the number of caps he won
for his country during his football career*

991.	Steve Archibald	5 Caps for England
992.	Jamie Redknapp	53 Caps for Republic of Ireland
993.	Kasey Keller	9 Caps for Nigeria
994.	Anthony Gardner	27 Caps for Scotland
995.	Ronny Rosenthal	36 Caps for Scotland
996.	Gordon Durie	17 Caps for England
997.	John Chiedozie	43 Caps for Scotland
998.	Chris Hughton	60 Caps for Israel
999.	Paul Walsh	102 Caps for USA
1000.	Colin Calderwood	1 Cap for England

ANSWERS

JÜRGEN KLINSMANN

1.   Ossie Ardiles

2.   20

3.   Sheffield Wednesday

4.   Everton

5.   Sampdoria

6.   Teddy Sheringham

7.   1964

8.   29

9.   Bayern Munich

10.   2004

HARRY REDKNAPP

11.   False: he never played a League game for Spurs

12.   2008

13.   Juande Ramos

14.   League Cup final

15.   Bolton Wanderers

16.   Daniel Levy

17.   Peter Crouch

18.   West Ham United

19.   1947

20.   8th

2009/2010

21.   Liverpool

22.   Jermain Defoe

23.   Burnley

24.   5

25.   Fulham

26.   Luka Modrić and Jermain Defoe

27.   Roman Pavlyuchenko

28.   Sébastien Bassong

29.   Sunderland

30.   Peter Crouch

HONOURS

31.	FA Cup Winners	1991
32.	Charity Shield Winners (joint)	1982
33.	League Cup Winners	1999
34.	Charity Shield Winners (joint)	1992
35.	FA Cup Winners	1981
36.	Peace Cup (Korea) Winners	2005
37.	League Cup Winners	2008
38.	FA Youth Cup Winners	1990
39.	FA Cup Winners	1982
40.	UEFA Cup Winners	1984

LEGENDS - 1

41.   Glenn Hoddle

42.   Teddy Sheringham

43.   Ossie Ardiles

44.   Ricky Villa

45.   David Ginola

46.   Gary Mabbutt

47.   Jermain Defoe

48.   Ray Clemence

49.   Garth Crooks

50.   Ian Walker

FA CUP WINNERS – 1991

51.   Nottingham Forest

52.   Erik Thorstvedt

53.   2-1 to Spurs (after extra time)

54.   Stuart Pearce

55.   Nayim and Paul Walsh

56.   Mark Crossley

57.   Erik Thorstvedt, Pat van den Hauwe, Gary Mabbutt, Steve
      Sedgley, Justin Edinburgh, David Howells, Paul Gascoigne, Paul
      Stewart, Paul Allen, Gary Lineker and Vinny Samways

58.   Des Walker

59.   Terry Venables

60.   Arsenal

MANAGERS

61.	Terry Venables	1987
62.	Gerry Francis	1994
63.	George Graham	1998
64.	Glenn Hoddle	2001
65.	Martin Jol	2004
66.	Christian Gross	1997
67.	Doug Livermore	1992
68.	Juande Ramos	2007
69.	David Pleat	1986
70.	Ossie Ardiles	1993

FIRST PREMIER LEAGUE SEASON – 1992/1993

71.   Southampton

72.   True: a 2-0 win at home against Sheffield United

73.   John Hendry

74.   16

75.   Teddy Sheringham

76.   Leeds United

77.	Southampton
78.	Gordon Durie
79.	8th
80.	Teddy Sheringham

LEAGUE GOALS – 1

81.	Chris Armstrong	48
82.	Darren Anderton	34
83.	Paul Allen	23
84.	Nico Claesen	18
85.	Sol Campbell	10
86.	Guy Butters	1
87.	Darren Bent	18
88.	Dimitar Berbatov	27
89.	Nick Barmby	20
90.	Clive Allen	60

WHERE DID THEY COME FROM? – 1

91.	Niko Kranjčar	Portsmouth
92.	Carlo Cudicini	Chelsea
93.	David Bentley	Blackburn Rovers
94.	Aaron Lennon	Leeds United
95.	Danny Murphy	Charlton Athletic
96.	Edgar Davids	Inter Milan
97.	Gareth Bale	Southampton
98.	Darren Bent	Charlton Athletic
99.	Chris Gunter	Cardiff City
100.	Heurelho Gomes	PSV Eindhoven

JERMAIN DEFOE

| 101. | Colin |

102.	West Ham United
103.	18
104.	Portsmouth
105.	Portsmouth
106.	West Ham United
107.	Portsmouth
108.	Leeds United
109.	13
110.	Holland

TEDDY SHERINGHAM

111.	Sheffield United
112.	1 (against Leeds United at home in a 4-0 win during February 1993)
113.	Manchester United
114.	Millwall (1984-91) and West Ham United (2004-07)
115.	18
116.	1966
117.	Newcastle United
118.	236: 230 (6)
119.	Glenn Hoddle
120.	97

2008/2009

121.	Aaron Lennon
122.	4-4
123.	Roman Pavlyuchenko
124.	Juande Ramos
125.	Pascal Chimbonda
126.	Darren Bent
127.	Liverpool

128.   *Carlo Cudicini*

129.   *Roman Pavlyuchenko*

130.   *8th*

OSSIE ARDILES

131.   *16*

132.   *Escape to Victory*

133.   *Nottingham Forest*

134.   *Blackburn Rovers, Queens Park Rangers and Swindon Town*

135.   *True*

136.   *5*

137.   *FA Cup (1981 and 1982) and UEFA Cup (1984)*

138.   *238: 222 (16)*

139.   *1993*

140.   *Argentinian*

LES FERDINAND

141.   *17*

142.   *Fulham*

143.   *Bolton Wanderers*

144.   *Gerry Francis*

145.   *West Ham United*

146.   *Striker*

147.   *33*

148.   *Aston Villa*

149.   *League Cup (1999)*

150.   *Newcastle United*

2007/2008

151.   *11th*

152.   *Robbie Keane and Dimitar Berbatov*

153. *Chelsea*

154. *Dimitar Berbatov*

155. *Gilberto*

156. *1-1*

157. *Dimitar Berbatov*

158. *Robbie Keane and Tom Huddlestone*

159. *Jonathan Woodgate*

160. *Younes Kaboul*

LEAGUE APPEARANCES - 1

161.	*David Tuttle*	*10 (3)*
162.	*Terry Yorath*	*44 (4)*
163.	*Sergei Rebrov*	*37 (22)*
164.	*David Kerslake*	*34 (3)*
165.	*Kazuyuki Toda*	*2 (2)*
166.	*Luke Young*	*44 (14)*
167.	*Andy Reid*	*20 (6)*
168.	*Ian Walker*	*257 (2)*
169.	*Neil Ruddock*	*45 (2)*
170.	*Teemu Tainio*	*48 (13)*

POT LUCK – 1

171. *Spurs or Lilywhites*

172. *2001*

173. *'To Dare is To Do'*

174. *Hewlett Packard*

175. *2 (1981 and 1982)*

176. *1971, 1973, 1999 and 2008*

177. *Jacques Santini (took over in 2004)*

178. *Michael Dawson*

179. *North*

180.   2005/06

CHRIS ARMSTRONG

181.   48

182.   Crystal Palace

183.   True: away against Everton during October 1995

184.   Manchester United

185.   1971

186.   Blackburn Rovers

187.   2

188.   Wrexham

189.   Liverpool

190.   Gerry Francis

LEAGUE APPEARANCES - 2

191.	Dean Richards	73
192.	Jamie Redknapp	37 (11)
193.	Garry Brady	0 (9)
194.	Gary Lineker	105
195.	Erik Edman	31
196.	Moussa Saïb	3 (10)
197.	Kevin Scott	16 (2)
198.	John Scales	29 (4)
199.	Johnnie Jackson	12 (8)
200.	Øyvind Leonhardsen	46 (8)

LEGENDS – 2

201.   Paul Allen

202.   Robbie Keane

203.   Ledley King

204.   Joe Kinnear

205.   Steve Perryman

206.   Gary Lineker

207.   Paul Gascoigne

208.   Clive Allen

209.   Chris Hughton

210.   David Howells

POT LUCK - 2

211.   True

212.   Ossie Ardiles (appointed manager in 1993)

213.   Swiss

214.   Thomson Holidays

215.   True

216.   Aaron Lennon

217.   2007

218.   £11 million

219.   1884

220.   Admiral

CLIVE ALLEN

221.   True

222.   Queens Park Rangers

223.   1961

224.   Les Allen

225.   105: 97 (8)

226.   Darren

227.   Everton

228.   Peter Shreeves

229.   60

230.   Bordeaux

WHERE DID THEY COME FROM? – 2

231.	Steve Hodge	Aston Villa
232.	Richard Gough	Dundee United
233.	Bobby Mimms	Everton
234.	Paul Walsh	Liverpool
235.	Steve Sedgley	Coventry City
236.	Justin Edinburgh	Southend United
237.	Pat Van Den Hauwe	Everton
238.	Teddy Sheringham	Nottingham Forest
239.	Clive Wilson	Queens Park Rangers
240.	Gica Popescu	PSV Eindhoven

GARETH BALE

241. Wales

242. 3

243. Southampton

244. Arsenal, Chelsea and Burnley

245. Fulham

246. 1989

247. 2 (during the 2007/08 season)

248. Football League Young Player of the Year award and Football Association of Wales Young Player of the Year award

249. Frank

250. True

LEAGUE GOALS – 2

251.	Simon Davies	13
252.	Stephen Kelly	2
253.	Micky Hazard	15
254.	Tony Galvin	20
255.	Gary Doherty	4

256.	Terry Fenwick	8
257.	Mark Falco	68
258.	Ilie Dumitrescu	4
259.	Ruel Fox	13
260.	Jason Dozzell	13

2006/2007

261.	5th
262.	Ricardo Rocha
263.	Dimitar Berbatov
264.	Michael Dawson and Aaron Lennon
265.	Charlton Athletic
266.	Robbie Keane
267.	Jermaine Jenas
268.	Paul Stalteri
269.	Aston Villa
270.	Paul Robinson

DIMITAR BERBATOV

271.	Bulgaria
272.	Bayer Leverkusen
273.	Sheffield United
274.	Fulham
275.	4
276.	1981
277.	False: he scored both goals
278.	27
279.	2008
280.	£10.9 million

DAVID GINOLA

281. 13

282. Aston Villa

283. PFA Players' Player of the Year and Football Writers' Player of the Year

284. League Cup (1999)

285. 1967

286. True

287. Newcastle United

288. Carlisle United

289. 100

290. Barnsley

2005/2006

291. True: 2-0 win against Portsmouth (away), 2-0 win against Middlesbrough (home) and 0-0 draw against Blackburn Rovers (away)

292. Blackburn Rovers

293. Robbie Keane

294. Paul Robinson

295. 16

296. 5th

297. Aaron Lennon

298. Michael Carrick

299. Martin Jol

300. Robbie Keane

SPURS IN THE FA CUP

301. 1901, 1921, 1961, 1962, 1967, 1981, 1982 and 1991

302. Arsenal

303. 6-1 to Newcastle United

304. *5th round (during March 1986)*

305. *Everton*

306. *Nayim*

307. *West Ham United*

308. *Robbie Keane*

309. *Manchester United*

310. *1987 (against Coventry City)*

LEAGUE GOALS – 3

311.	*Dean Marney*	*2*
312.	*Steed Malbranque*	*6*
313.	*Mbulelo Mabizela*	*1*
314.	*Steve Perryman*	*31*
315.	*Noé Pamarot*	*1*
316.	*Noureddine Naybet*	*1*
317.	*Nayim*	*11*
318.	*John Moncur*	*1*
319.	*Mido*	*1*
320.	*Pedro Mendes*	*13*

WHERE DID THEY GO? – 1

321.	*Kevin Boateng*	*Portsmouth*
322.	*Gordon Durie*	*Rangers*
323.	*John Polston*	*Norwich City*
324.	*Paul Walsh*	*Portsmouth*
325.	*Paul Stewart*	*Liverpool*
326.	*John Moncur*	*Swindon Town*
327.	*Phil Gray*	*Luton Town*
328.	*Richard Gough*	*Rangers*
329.	*Chris Gunter*	*Nottingham Forest*
330.	*Ian Crook*	*Norwich City*

LEAGUE GOALS – 4

331.	Andy Reid	1
332.	Graham Roberts	23
333.	Ronny Rosenthal	4
334.	Neil Ruddock	3
335.	Paul Stewart	28
336.	Paul Stalteri	2
337.	Andy Turner	3
338.	Ramon Vega	7
339.	Ricardo Villa	18
340.	Mauricio Taricco	2

SPURS IN THE LEAGUE CUP

341. 1971, 1973, 1999 and 2008
342. 5-1 to Spurs
343. Chris Armstrong
344. Sol Campbell
345. Southend United
346. Hartlepool United
347. Vinny Samways
348. Oldham Athletic
349. 5-1 to Spurs
350. 1982

WHERE DID THEY COME FROM? – 3

351.	John Scales	Liverpool
352.	Ramon Vega	Cagliari
353.	José Dominguez	Sporting Lisbon
354.	Nicola Berti	Inter Milan
355.	Mauricio Taricco	Ipswich Town
356.	Anthony Gardner	Port Vale

357.	Gary Doherty	Luton Town
358.	Neil Sullivan	Wimbledon
359.	Chris Perry	Wimbledon
360.	Øyvind Leonhardsen	Liverpool

LEAGUE CUP FINALISTS - 2009

361. Manchester United

362. 0-0

363. 88,217

364. Ben Foster (Manchester United's goalkeeper)

365. Michael Dawson and Ledley King

366. Jamie O'Hara, Gareth Bale and David Bentley

367. Harry Redknapp

368. 5 (Michael Dawson, Ledley King, Aaron Lennon, Jermaine Jenas and Darren Bent)

369. March (1 March 2009)

370. Burnley (Spurs won 4-1 at home and lost 3-2 away)

WHERE DID THEY GO? – 2

371.	Gudni Bergsson	Bolton Wanderers
372.	Gica Popescu	Barcelona
373.	Kevin Scott	Norwich City
374.	Dean Austin	Crystal Palace
375.	Ronny Rosenthal	Watford
376.	Clive Wilson	Cambridge United
377.	Jason Cundy	Ipswich Town
378.	Steve Slade	Queens Park Rangers
379.	Darren Caskey	Reading
380.	Vinny Samways	Everton

LEAGUE CUP WINNERS - 2008

381. Chelsea

382. Juande Ramos

383. Paul Robinson

384. 1-1 (with Spurs scoring in extra time to win 2-1)

385. Dimitar Berbatov

386. Pascal Chimbonda and Steed Malbranque

387. True

388. Mark Halsey

389. True

390. Jonathan Woodgate (in the 94th minute)

WHERE DID THEY GO? – 3

391. Ramon Vega   Watford

392. Milenko Ačimovič   Lille

393. Chris Perry   Charlton Athletic

394. Gary Doherty   Norwich City

395. Steffen Iversen   Wolves

396. Stephen Clemence   Birmingham City

397. Ben Thatcher   Leicester City

398. Jamie Redknapp   Southampton

399. Neil Sullivan   Chelsea

400. Alton Thelwell   Hull City

TERRY VENABLES

401. 5

402. True

403. 13th

404. Bill Nicholson

405. 115: 114 (1)

406. Chelsea

407. *El Tel*

408. *England*

409. *FA Cup winners' medal in 1967*

410. *1943*

2004/2005

411. *Frederic Kanoute (2), Ledley King and Stephen Kelly*

412. *2-0 to Tottenham*

413. *Dean Marney*

414. *Liverpool*

415. *Michael Dawson*

416. *Jermain Defoe (13) and Robbie Keane (11)*

417. *Radek Černý (he also made 1 substitute appearance against Aston Villa during May 2005)*

418. *14*

419. *Michael Carrick*

420. *Jermain Defoe*

GARTH CROOKS

421. *True*

422. *FA Cup winners' medals in 1981 and 1982 and UEFA Cup medal in 1984*

423. *Anthony*

424. *1980*

425. *16 (during the 1980/81 season)*

426. *Nottingham Forest (during August 1980)*

427. *Forward*

428. *48*

429. *True*

430. *West Bromwich Albion*

LEAGUE CUP WINNERS - 1999

431.   Leicester City

432.   Allan Nielsen

433.   George Graham

434.   5 (Ian Walker, Sol Campbell, Justin Edinburgh, Darren Anderton and Les Ferdinand)

435.   Steffen Freund

436.   March (21 March 2009)

437.   Worthington Cup

438.   77,892

439.   Ramon Vega

440.   Wimbledon (0-0 draw at home and 1-0 away win)

DARREN ANDERTON

441.   Portsmouth

442.   6

443.   League Cup (1999)

444.   299: 273 (26)

445.   Southampton

446.   Leeds United

447.   Southampton

448.   False: he scored 26

449.   Robert

450.   7

MARK FALCO

451.   174: 162 (12)

452.   Keith Burkinshaw

453.   22

454.   True

455.   Striker

456. *1960*

457. *68*

458. *Bolton Wanderers*

459. *UEFA Cup winner in 1984*

460. *Watford*

PAUL STEWART

461. *Blackpool*

462. *True: in the 53rd minute*

463. *Manchester City*

464. *28*

465. *Terry Venables*

466. *Manchester United*

467. *Andrew*

468. *131: 126 (5)*

469. *True: he won 3 full international caps during his football career*

470. *Liverpool*

PETER SHREEVES

471. *True*

472. *1940*

473. *3rd (during the 1984/85 season)*

474. *David Pleat*

475. *1991/92*

476. *False: he never played for Spurs*

477. *Chelsea*

478. *False: he has never managed England*

479. *Inside forward*

480. *2 (1984-86 and 1991-92)*

PAUL GASCOIGNE

481.   19

482.   Newcastle United

483.   1992

484.   True

485.   6

486.   FA Cup winners' medal in 1991

487.   Kettering Town

488.   92: 91(1)

489.   John

490.   Midfielder

2003/2004

491.   Robbie Keane

492.   Leicester City

493.   Wolves

494.   13

495.   David Pleat

496.   Gus Poyet

497.   14

498.   Kasey Keller

499.   Michael Brown

500.   Stéphane Dalmat

RICKY VILLA

501.   18

502.   1952

503.   FA Cup winners' medals in 1981 and 1982

504.   Central midfielder

505.   Keith Burkinshaw

506.   Argentinian

507. *1978*

508. *1981/82*

509. *Nottingham Forest*

510. *133: 124 (9)*

CHRIS WADDLE

511. *33*

512. *Sheffield Wednesday*

513. *1960*

514. *Marseille*

515. *6*

516. *Roland*

517. *Watford*

518. *138: 137 (1)*

519. *Newcastle United*

520. *14*

PAUL WALSH

521. *1962*

522. *Manchester United*

523. *Liverpool*

524. *19*

525. *False: he was an Arsenal fan*

526. *FA Cup winner in 1991*

527. *Striker*

528. *True: he won 5 caps, scoring 1 goal*

529. *Portsmouth*

530. *128: 84 (44)*

CHRISTIAN ZIEGE

531. *German*

532. *2001*

533. *True*

534. *7*

535. *Arsenal*

536. *Middlesbrough*

537. *5 (during the 2001/02 season)*

538. *True: Tottenham equaliser after 33 minutes*

539. *Glenn Hoddle*

540. *47: 44 (3)*

2002/2003

541. *Robbie Keane*

542. *True: Spurs lost 5-1 away to Middlesbrough and 4-0 at home to Blackburn Rovers*

543. *2-0 to Tottenham (Teddy Sheringham and Robbie Keane scoring the goals)*

544. *Charlton Athletic*

545. *Robbie Keane (13 goals) and Teddy Sheringham (12 goals)*

546. *Kasey Keller*

547. *5*

548. *Gus Poyet*

549. *Charlton Athletic (12th), Fulham (14th) and West Ham United (18th)*

550. *Robbie Keane*

UEFA CUP WINNERS - 1984

551. *Paul Miller*

552. *Tony Parks, Danny Thomas, Chris Hughton, Graham Roberts, Paul Miller, Gary Mabbutt, Micky Hazard, Gary Stevens, Tony Galvin, Steve Archibald and Mark Falco*

553. *Keith Burkinshaw*

554. Graham Roberts

555. May 1984

556. 46,258

557. Hajduk Split

558. Steve Archibald and Mark Falco

559. Graham Roberts, Mark Falco, Gary Stevens and Steve Archibald

560. Graham Roberts

GERRY FRANCIS

561. 1994 (19 November was the day of his first match against Aston Villa)

562. 10th

563. David Ginola

564. Bristol Rovers

565. Christian Gross

566. False: he never played for Spurs during his playing career

567. 1951

568. Queens Park Rangers

569. Semi-finals, then losing 4-1 at Elland Road against Everton

570. 7th (during the 1994/95 season)

GLENN HODDLE

571. 88

572. 2001

573. 'Diamond Lights'

574. 377: 370 (7)

575. Terry Neill

576. AS Monaco

577. True

578. 2 (1981 and 1982)

579. 1957

580.   *England*

CHRIS HUGHTON

581.   *Fullback*

582.   *53*

583.   *2 (1981 and 1982)*

584.   *3*

585.   *West Ham United*

586.   *Newcastle United*

587.   *12*

588.   *Manchester City*

589.   *1958*

590.   *297: 293 (4)*

2001/2002

591.   *Dean Richards*

592.   *Gus Poyet and Teddy Sheringham*

593.   *Neil Sullivan*

594.   *Gus Poyet*

595.   *14*

596.   *Kasey Keller*

597.   *Glenn Hoddle*

598.   *Gus Poyet*

599.   *Manchester United*

600.   *9*

TOM HUDDLESTONE

601.   *Derby County*

602.   *Fabio Capello*

603.   *3*

604.   *1986*

605.   *Martin Jol*

606. Andrew

607. Sunderland

608. True

609. Port Vale

610. True: against Dynamo Zagreb (in a 4-0 home win during November 2008) and against Spartak Moscow (in a 2-2 home draw during December 2008)

DAVID HOWELLS

611. 1 (against Blackburn Rovers in a 2-0 away win during November 1992)

612. 1967

613. True

614. 277: 238 (39)

615. English

616. 22

617. Southampton

618. Midfielder

619. Chelsea (at home in a 2-1 defeat during February 1997) and West Ham United (away in a 4-3 defeat during February 1997)

620. Peter Shreeves

FA CUP WINNERS - 1981

621. Ricky Villa

622. Manchester City

623. Tommy Hutchison

624. Milija Aleksic

625. Keith Burkinshaw

626. 'Ossie's Dream'

627. Milija Aleksic, Chris Hughton, Paul Miller, Graham Roberts, Ricky Villa, Steve Perryman, Ossie Ardiles, Steve Archibald, Tony Galvin, Glenn Hoddle and Garth Crooks

628. True

629. 1-1

630. 6th

2000/2001

631. Ben Thatcher

632. 9

633. Neil Sullivan

634. Tim Sherwood

635. Coventry City

636. Gary Doherty

637. Willem Korsten

638. Ipswich Town

639. 2

640. Les Ferdinand

LEAGUE HAT-TRICKS

641.	v. Leeds United, February 1993	Teddy Sheringham
642.	v. Everton, December 1998	Chris Armstrong
643.	v. Everton, January 2003	Robbie Keane
644.	v. Wigan Athletic, November 2009	Jermain Defoe
645.	v. Sunderland, March 1997	Steffen Iversen
646.	v. Wimbledon, May 1998	Jürgen Klinsmann
647.	v. Southampton, December 2004	Jermain Defoe
648.	v. Leicester City, November 2000	Les Ferdinand
649.	v. Hull City, August 2009	Jermain Defoe
650.	v. Newcastle United, December 1994	Teddy Sheringham

TIM SHERWOOD

651. 12

652. Blackburn Rovers

653. Coventry City

654. False: he was 30 when he made his full debut in England's 3-1 victory over Poland at Wembley during March 1999

655. 1969

656. Watford

657. Central midfielder

658. Arsenal

659. George Graham

660. 93: 81 (12)

1999/2000

661. Southampton

662. Steffen Iversen

663. Chris Armstrong

664. 3-1 to Tottenham

665. Newcastle United

666. George Graham

667. Steffen Iversen and Chris Armstrong

668. Ian Walker

669. 15

670. False: won 1, drew 1 and lost 2

JERMAINE JENAS

671. Newcastle United

672. Liverpool

673. Everton

674. Anthony

675. Switzerland

676. 6

677. Burnley

678. 1983

679.   West Bromwich Albion

680.   Nottingham Forest

KEITH BURKINSHAW

681.   2 (1981 and 1982)

682.   False: he never played for Spurs in his playing days

683.   Harry

684.   1984

685.   UEFA Cup (1984)

686.   Defender

687.   West Bromwich Albion

688.   1935

689.   Terry Neill

690.   True

ROBBIE KEANE

691.   West Ham United

692.   Everton

693.   Bolton Wanderers

694.   Burnley

695.   16

696.   Republic of Ireland

697.   Inter Milan

698.   Liverpool

699.   Glenn Hoddle (in 2002)

700.   1980

JUANDE RAMOS

701.   Blackpool

702.   Robbie Keane and Pascal Chimbonda

703.   21

704.   *True*

705.   *Sevilla*

706.   *11th*

707.   *1954*

708.   *Midfielder*

709.   *League Cup (2008)*

710.   *Real Madrid*

1998/1999

711.   *11 (7 at home and 4 away)*

712.   *Colin Calderwood*

713.   *Steffen Iversen*

714.   *Les Ferdinand*

715.   *4-1 to Tottenham*

716.   *Steffen Iversen and David Ginola*

717.   *Sol Campbell*

718.   *Christian Gross*

719.   *Sol Campbell*

720.   *Mauricio Taricco*

LEDLEY KING

721.   *Brenton*

722.   *26*

723.   *USA*

724.   *George Graham*

725.   *Bradford City*

726.   *Liverpool*

727.   *Central defender*

728.   *True*

729.   *Mexico*

730.   *1980*

AARON LENNON

731. Leeds United

732. True

733. 5

734. Chelsea

735. Birmingham City

736. USA and Algeria

737. 7

738. £1 million

739. Justin

740. Chelsea

1997/1998

741. Jürgen Klinsmann, David Ginola and Ramon Vega

742. Allan Nielsen

743. Nicola Berti

744. False: won 1, drew 3 and lost 1

745. Derby County

746. 14th

747. Jürgen Klinsmann

748. Gerry Francis

749. José Dominguez

750. Jürgen Klinsmann

GARY LINEKER

751. 67

752. 1989

753. True

754. Turkey

755. Leicester

756. Everton (his only season playing for Everton)

757.   48

758.   Winston

759.   105

760.   Nagoya Grampus Eight

GARY MABBUTT

761.   27

762.   1998

763.   Nottingham Forest

764.   True: he scored for Tottenham in the 40th minute and for
        Coventry in the 96th minute

765.   Ray Mabbutt (father) and Kevin Mabbutt (brother)

766.   Bristol Rovers

767.   FA Cup

768.   16

769.   Centre back

770.   1961

NAYIM

771.   Barcelona

772.   112: 95 (17)

773.   Terry Venables

774.   Norwich City

775.   Midfielder

776.   True

777.   Manchester City

778.   11

779.   FA Cup (1991)

780.   Real Zaragoza

GEORGE GRAHAM

781. *Leeds United (1996-98)*

782. *The League Cup*

783. *1944*

784. *11th (during the 1998/99 season)*

785. *Sergei Rebrov*

786. *Tim Sherwood*

787. *39%*

788. *10th*

789. *Scotland*

790. *2001*

1996/1997

791. *7*

792. *Espen Baardsen*

793. *Southampton*

794. *False: Tottenham drew 1 and lost 2*

795. *Steffen Iversen*

796. *Gerry Francis*

797. *13*

798. *John Scales*

799. *Sol Campbell*

800. *Newcastle United*

ROMAN PAVLYUCHENKO

801. *Russian*

802. *5*

803. *Aston Villa*

804. *Bolton Wanderers*

805. *9*

806. *Striker*

807. Newcastle United

808. Blackburn Rovers

809. 1981

810. Spartak Moscow

FA CUP WINNERS - 1982

811. Ray Clemence

812. 1-0

813. Queens Park Rangers

814. Chris Hughton (Irish), Steve Archibald (Scottish) and Tony Galvin (Irish)

815. Leicester City

816. 7th

817. True: they won the FA Cup in 1981, beating Manchester City

818. Steve Perryman

819. Glenn Hoddle

820. Keith Burkinshaw

STEVE PERRYMAN

821. 1951

822. Sunderland

823. 2

824. 20

825. 2 (1981 and 1982)

826. 655: 653 (2)

827. Oxford United

828. Iceland

829. 1982

830. 31

1995/1996

831. *Ruel Fox, Teddy Sheringham and David Howells*

832. *Chris Armstrong*

833. *Tottenham (8th place; Chelsea finished in 11th place)*

834. *0-0*

835. *16*

836. *Chris Armstrong*

837. *Gerry Francis*

838. *Darren Caskey*

839. *Leeds United*

840. *Darren Anderton*

GUS POYET

841. *Chelsea*

842. *Midfielder*

843. *Uruguay*

844. *82: 66 (16)*

845. *Glenn Hoddle*

846. *Tranmere Rovers*

847. *Real Zaragoza*

848. *Portsmouth*

849. *Brighton & Hove Albion*

850. *18*

MARTIN JOL

851. *2004 (November)*

852. *Jacques Santini (during June 2004)*

853. *True (during December 2004)*

854. *1956*

855. *5th*

856. *Midfielder*

857. *West Bromwich Albion (1982-84) and Coventry City (1984-85)*

858. *Ajax*

859. *Juande Ramos*

860. *True: he won 3 full international caps for The Netherlands*

1994/1995

861. *Sheffield Wednesday*

862. *Ossie Ardiles*

863. *Gica Popescu*

864. *Nick Barmby and Teddy Sheringham*

865. *4-0 to Tottenham*

866. *Jürgen Klinsmann*

867. *Tottenham (7th place; Chelsea finished 11th and Arsenal finished 12th)*

868. *Gudni Bergsson*

869. *Teddy Sheringham*

870. *Aston Villa*

GRAHAM ROBERTS

871. *209: 200 (9)*

872. *True: he won 6 caps for England*

873. *FA Cup (1981 and 1982) and UEFA Cup (1984)*

874. *Chelsea*

875. *Central defender*

876. *Paul*

877. *Hard As Nails*

878. *Rangers*

879. *23*

880. *Stoke City*

1993/1994

881. Teddy Sheringham

882. Darren Caskey, Micky Hazard and Vinny Samways

883. 11

884. Ronny Rosenthal

885. Oldham Athletic

886. True

887. David Kerslake

888. Southampton

889. Jason Dozzell and Teddy Sheringham

890. Gordon Durie

PAUL ROBINSON

891. 137

892. 2004

893. Leeds United

894. Watford

895. League Cup winner (2008)

896. 41

897. True

898. 1

899. William

900. Blackburn Rovers

VINNY SAMWAYS

901. 193: 165 (28)

902. Everton

903. True

904. Midfielder (central)

905. 3

906. False: he never won a full international cap, but he did play for England at under-21 level

907. **Nottingham Forest**

908. *1968*

909. **Walsall**

910. *11*

DAVID PLEAT

911. *1986/87*

912. **John**

913. *3rd*

914. **True**

915. **Luton Town**

916. *1998*

917. **False**

918. **Winger**

919. **Sheffield Wednesday**

920. *1945*

SQUAD NUMBERS – 2010/2011

921.	Kyle Walker	28
922.	Younes Kaboul	4
923.	Wilson Palacios	12
924.	Roman Pavlyuchenko	9
925.	Heurelho Gomes	1
926.	Sébastien Bassong	19
927.	Danny Rose	25
928.	David Bentley	5
929.	Jonathan Woodgate	39
930.	Jermaine Jenas	8

WHITE HART LANE

931. **N17 0AP**

932. **Notts County**

933. **1995**

934. **True**

935. **Seven Sisters**

936. **Sunderland**

937. **1899**

938. **West Stand**

939. **100 metres x 67 metres**

940. **White Hart Lane**

CLUB HISTORY

941. **1882**

942. **Rafael van der Vaart**

943. **Young Boys**

944. **FC Twente, Inter Milan and Werder Bremen**

945. **1901**

946. **Peter Crouch (against Young Boys)**

947. **4th**

948. **Bristol Rovers**

949. **William Gallas**

950. **Holsten**

LEAGUE APPEARANCES - 3

951.	**Timothée Atouba**	**15 (3)**
952.	**Young-Pyo Lee**	**68 (2)**
953.	**Micky Hazard**	**88 (31)**
954.	**Mark Bowen**	**14 (3)**
955.	**Paul Gascoigne**	**91 (1)**
956.	**Rory Allen**	**10 (11)**
957.	**Chris Fairclough**	**60**
958.	**Hossam Ghaly**	**17 (4)**

959.	Espen Baardsen	22 (1)
960.	Andy Gray	23 (10)

SQUAD NUMBERS – 1994/1995

961.	Gheorghe Popescu	4
962.	Ian Walker	13
963.	Sol Campbell	23
964.	Ronny Rosenthal	11
965.	Justin Edinburgh	3
966.	Ilie Dumitrescu	8
967.	David Howells	15
968.	David Kerslake	22
969.	Nick Barmby	7
970.	Stuart Nethercott	14

LEAGUE APPEARANCES - 4

971.	Gerry Armstrong	65 (19)
972.	Dean Austin	117 (7)
973.	Matthew Etherington	20 (25)
974.	Ian Crook	10 (10)
975.	Ray Clemence	240
976.	Michael Carrick	61 (3)
977.	Colin Calderwood	152 (11)
978.	Stéphane Dalmat	12 (10)
979.	Edgar Davids	28 (3)
980.	Sean Davis	11 (4)

POSITIONS IN THE LEAGUE

981.	1980/81	10th in Division One
982.	1981/82	4th in Division One
983.	1982/83	4th in Division One

984.	1983/84	8th in Division One
985.	1984/85	3rd in Division One
986.	1985/86	10th in Division One
987.	1986/87	3rd in Division One
988.	1987/88	13th in Division One
989.	1988/89	6th in Division One
990.	1989/90	3rd in Division One

INTERNATIONALS

991.	Steve Archibald	27 Caps for Scotland
992.	Jamie Redknapp	17 Caps for England
993.	Kasey Keller	102 Caps for USA
994.	Anthony Gardner	1 Cap for England
995.	Ronny Rosenthal	60 Caps for Israel
996.	Gordon Durie	43 Caps for Scotland
997.	John Chiedozie	9 Caps for Nigeria
998.	Chris Hughton	53 Caps for Republic of Ireland
999.	Paul Walsh	5 Caps for England
1000.	Colin Calderwood	36 Caps for Scotland

NOTES:

NOTES:

NOTES:

NOTES:

NOTES:

OTHER BOOKS BY CHRIS COWLIN:

* Celebrities' Favourite Football Teams

* The British TV Sitcom Quiz Book

* The Cricket Quiz Book

* The Gooners Quiz Book

* The Horror Film Quiz Book

* The Official Aston Villa Quiz Book

* The Official Birmingham City Quiz Book

* The Official Brentford Quiz Book

* The Official Bristol Rovers Quiz Book

* The Official Burnley Quiz Book

* The Official Bury Quiz Book

* The Official Carlisle United Quiz Book

* The Official Carry On Quiz Book

* The Official Chesterfield Football Club Quiz Book

* The Official Colchester United Quiz Book

* The Official Coventry City Quiz Book

* The Official Doncaster Rovers Quiz Book

* The Official Greenock Morton Quiz Book

* The Official Heart of Midlothian Quiz Book

* The Official Hereford United Quiz Book

* The Official Hull City Quiz Book

* The Official Ipswich Town Quiz Book

OTHER BOOKS BY CHRIS COWLIN:

* The Official Leicester City Quiz Book

* The Official Macclesfield Town Quiz Book

* The Official Norwich City Football Club Quiz

* The Official Notts County Quiz Book

* The Official Peterborough United Quiz Book

* The Official Port Vale Quiz Book

* The Official Queen of the South Quiz Book

* The Official Rochdale AFC Quiz Book

* The Official Rotherham United Quiz Book

* The Official Sheffield United Quiz Book

* The Official Shrewsbury Town Quiz Book

* The Official Stockport County Quiz Book

* The Official Walsall Football Club Quiz Book

* The Official Watford Football Club Quiz Book

* The Official West Bromwich Albion Quiz Book

* The Official Wolves Quiz Book

* The Official Yeovil Town Quiz Book

* The Reality Television Quiz Book

* The Southend United Quiz Book

* The Spurs Quiz Book

* The Sunderland AFC Quiz Book

* The Ultimate Derby County Quiz Book

* The West Ham United Quiz Book

www.apexpublishing.co.uk